PRENTICE-HALL, INC., Englewood Cliffs, N.J.

To my son

Nine Men's Morris and Over 800 Other Indoor Games, Puzzles and Stunts for All Ages by Darwin A. Hindman, Ph.D. Published in original form under the titles *The Complete Book of Games and Stunts, Handbook of Indoor Games* and *Stunts and Handbook of Active Games*, copyright © 1956, 1955 and 1951, respectively, by Prentice-Hall, Inc.

Printed in the United States of America
Prentice-Hall International, Inc., London
Prentice-Hall of Australia, Pty. Ltd., Sydney
Prentice-Hall of Canada, Ltd., Toronto
Prentice-Hall of India Private Ltd., New Delhi
Prentice-Hall of Japan, Inc., Tokyo
Prentice-Hall of Southeast Asia Pte. Ltd., Singapore
Whitehall Books Limited, Wellington, New Zealand
10 9 8 7 6 5 4

Library of Congress Cataloging in Publication Data

Hindman, Darwin Alexander
    Nine men's Morris, and over 800 other indoor games, puzzles, and stunts for all ages.

    Originally published under title: Handbook of indoor games and stunts.
    SUMMARY: A collection of puzzles, brain teasers, and nonathletic games including contests and stunts.
    1. Indoor games.   [1. Indoor games.   2. Games.
3. Puzzles]   I. Title.
[GV1229.H5 1978]   793   77-13029
ISBN 0-13-622530-6 pbk.

TABLE OF CONTENTS

PREFACE

THIS BOOK DESCRIBES GAMES, INCLUDING CONTESTS AND STUNTS, THAT are nonathletic, that is, those that do not involve strenuous muscular activity. Part One is concerned with games that are purely "mental," not based at all on muscular skill; for lack of a better term they are, with some misgiving, called "Quiet Games and Stunts." Part Two includes games that require some muscular skill but do not involve activity strenuous enough for them to be classed as athletic. Part Three is a selected collection of puzzles and brain teasers, with solutions.

The whole collection is organized logically, and is unusually complete, although some of the most highly organized games, such as checkers, chess, and the standard card games, have been omitted intentionally.

DARWIN A. HINDMAN

Part One

QUIET GAMES AND STUNTS

Chapter I

MIXERS

A "MIXER" IS AN ORGANIZED ACTIVITY USED TO ACQUAINT THE MEMBERS of a group with one another, to form them into partnerships or teams, and to eliminate undesired inhibitions. Many of the games to be described in later chapters serve these purposes very well, but this chapter is concerned only with activities that are not competitive and that have no purposes other than those of the mixer.

Section I: Get-acquainted mixers

GROUP A: PLAYERS ARE IN DEFINITE FORMATION

1. RECEIVING LINE

This is the standard receiving line used at receptions and other relatively formal gatherings; but it need not be stiff, and under some conditions it is very desirable even on informal occasions. Its most important function is that of introducing a few visitors, newcomers, or notables to other guests.

The receiving line itself consists of the hosts and the special guests, together with officers, committee chairmen, or others in positions of responsibility. Each guest in turn introduces himself to the first member of the line and is introduced by the latter to the second member. He continues to the end of the line, being introduced by each person in the line to the next one. Thus, those standing in the receiving line meet all the other guests, but the other guests do not meet one another.

2. CONTINUOUS RECEIVING LINE

Through this modification of the Receiving Line, each person in a gathering is introduced to all the others. The standard receiving line is formed, and each guest goes through it as usual. However, after he has gone down the line, he steps into place at the end and receives the later arrivals.

3. CIRCLE CHAT

The players form two concentric circles. Commonly, but not necessarily, men form one circle and women the other. The leader announces a subject for conversation, and each player must engage in a discussion on that topic with his nearest neighbor in the other circle. After one or two minutes, the leader gives a signal and each player then moves to the left a prescribed number of spaces, beginning a conversation with a new partner on a new topic announced by the leader. This change of partners may be repeated as often as desired.

This game may also be played to music, with the two circles marching in opposite directions. When the music stops, each player halts and begins a conversation on an announced topic with the person in the other circle beside whom he stands. Naturally, the topics selected should be those likely to lead to comical discussion.

4. MIXING CIRCLE

This game is the same as Circle Chat except that the leader may specify a stunt or movement of some sort to be performed by all the couples. For example, he might say, "Join hands and skip around three times," or "Bark like a dog." The stunt may be called for instead of, or in addition to, the conversation.

5. INQUISITION

The formation and movement of the players in Inquisition are the same as in Circle Chat. However, no topic for conversation is given; instead each player must find out as much as possible about his partner. At the close of each period, the leader calls any couple from their positions and quizzes them about each other.

6. SHAKE

This variation of Circle Chat has an added feature: Each time a player acquires a new partner he must greet him with a handshake, and in so doing must use the kind of handshake specified by the leader. The leader may announce the method, hold up a card bearing the name of the method, or demonstrate with the aid of another person. Of course, the various shakes should be exaggerated and made as comical as possible. Some suggested methods are: the "fish," with hands held limply; the "pumphandle"; the "highbrow."

7. CHAIN INTRODUCTIONS

The players stand or sit in a circle with the leader standing in the center. The leader, addressing the group as a whole, says, "How do you do? My name is Alice Jones" (giving her real name, of course). A designated player then walks up to Alice from his place in the circle and says, "How do you do, Alice Jones? My name is Jim Barnes." The next person to the left then comes forward and says, "How do you do Alice Jones and Jim Barnes? My name is Peggy Anderson." This cumulative process is continued, each person naming all those who have already introduced themselves and adding his own name, until some player fails. The game is then begun again, with a new starter. The type of name used may vary with the situation; for example, instead of introducing herself as Alice Jones, a player might say Miss Jones, or simply Alice.

Each player must pronounce his name in such a way that all can hear and understand it. A good leader will not permit mumbling and will see to it that names are understood even if he has to spell them. Obviously, this mixer has no place in a gathering where all players know each other well.

8. BUNCH OF KEYS

All players except one stand in a circle. The odd player stands inside the circle, holding a large bunch of keys. He steps up to any player in the circle and the two introduce themselves. The odd man then proceeds around the circle in a clockwise direction, greeting each second person. Each of these circle players, after introducing himself to the odd man, starts around the circle in a counterclockwise direction. He also greets each second player. Furthermore, any player in the circle who has been greeted by any other player starts around the circle in a direction opposite that taken by his greeter, and he introduces himself to each second player. When a very great confusion results, the odd man drops the bunch of keys to the floor. At this signal, all resume their original places and a new game is begun.

GROUP B: PLAYERS MOVE AT RANDOM

9. AUTOGRAPH MIXER

Each player is given a pencil and a small card or folder. He is directed to obtain the autographs of all others present—perhaps also their addresses, occupations, or other information appropriate to the occasion. This mixer is simple, but extremely effective in a gathering where the members are not well acquainted.

10. LEFT-HANDED MIXER

As each guest arrives, he is instructed to shake hands with each of the other guests, using only his left hand. It is assumed, of course, that as he shakes hands he will introduce himself to all those he does not know. This mixer may be combined with the Autograph Mixer, with all writing done with the left hand.

11. SACK SHAKE

An ordinary paper sack is given to each guest on arrival. He must wear this sack on his right hand and shake hands with all the other guests while wearing it.

12. MILLIONAIRE COUPLE

A coin is given secretly to one of the couples. The two do not stay together, but join each other from time to time. The other players try to identify the couple and the first one who finds them together and asks, "Are you the millionaire couple?" gets the coin.

13. GIFT SHAKE

A coin, a box of candy, or some other object that is small but desirable is given secretly to each one of several players. It is announced that certain unidentified players have valuable objects and that each will present his object to the tenth person who shakes hands with him. No other explanation is needed.

14. BINGO MIXER

Each player is given a card showing a diagram of squares, the number of squares corresponding to the number of guests present. The diagram consists of the required number of horizontal rows of four or five squares each. The player then gets the autographs of all the others, one autograph in each square. When all autographs have been obtained, the leader calls names at random, preferably from slips drawn from a bowl or hat. As each name is called, the players check it off on their cards, and the first one to check all the names in any horizontal row is the winner.

15. MUSICAL MIXER

Each player is handed a slip on which is the name of a well-known song, each song name being given to several players. Each player must find the other members of his group. When a group has been formed, its members converse among themselves for awhile and then the groups take turns in singing their songs.

16. CHIEF'S ORDERS

Each person is assigned a number, which is written on a card pinned to his clothing where it can be seen easily; it is best for men to have odd, and women even, numbers. Each person is also given a list of "orders," things that he must do, one after another. These "orders" must all require doing something that involves other players.

A few suggestions:

Tabulate the brands of cigarettes smoked by all the men.
Find number 6 and help her select the most handsome men.
Find number 3 and introduce him to number 8.
Make a list of the brown-eyed women.
Find number 10 and help him list the women whose first names begin with A.
Ask number 11 about the movies he has seen recently.
Talk with number 4 about baseball.

Section II: Partner mixers

Many social games and other activities are played by people in pairs or other small groups. Of course, these groups can be formed in a variety of ways with no difficulty, but it is best that they be formed by some device that is in itself a good social activity and that serves as a mixer or ice-breaker. Some of these devices are described in this section.

GROUP A: MATCH FOR PARTNERS

The most common method of obtaining partners involves matching
—actual objects, words, ideas, actions, or the like. Objects, words,
or instructions are distributed at random and for each item there is
a corresponding one. Each player must then find the other player
who has the matching item. It is this seeking and finding that
provides the fun.

17. ANIMAL PARTNERS

The names of animals having familiar calls are selected, and each
name is written on two slips of paper. One set of the slips is distributed at random among the girls, the other among the boys. Then
each player does his best to imitate the call of his animal, at the
same time trying to locate the other player who is giving the same
call. Of course, there must be no talking.

18. SONG PARTNERS

Well-known tunes are selected, and the name of each is written
on two slips of paper. One set of song names is distributed at
random among the girls, the other among the boys. Each player
then sings or hums his tune and tries to find, as his partner, the
other person who is singing the same song.

19. ACTION PARTNERS

Two identical sets of slips of paper are prepared, each slip containing the name of someone whose actions can be imitated. In most
cases the slips will refer to a class of persons—golf player, orchestra
leader, skater, and the like; but it is permissible to name a single
person, for example, Charlie Chaplin. Each person imitates, *in
pantomime only*, the character named on his slip and claims as a
partner the other person who is imitating the same character.

20. MATCHING OBJECTS

Two identical sets of objects are prepared. One set is distributed
among the boys, the other among the girls. Each player then finds,
and keeps as his partner, the other player who has the duplicate
of his object. Objects such as playing cards, marbles, flowers, pictures cut from magazines, or even pieces of paper cut into different

shapes can be used. It is often better for the objects to have some connection with the occasion. At a Hallowe'en party, pictures of brooms, pumpkins, witches, and the like, might be distributed; or if paper hats are to be worn at a party, the hats themselves might be the objects to be matched for partners.

21. MATCHING SHOES

Each girl removes one shoe. All the shoes are collected, thoroughly mixed, and distributed among the boys, one shoe to a boy. Then each boy must find his partner, the girl who is wearing a shoe that makes a pair with the one he holds.

22. MATCHING HALVES

A number of pictures are clipped from advertisements in magazines. Each picture is cut into two parts. One part is given to a boy, the other to a girl. Each player obtains his partner by finding the person who holds the other half of his picture.

23. MATCH THE CUT

A set of figures, identical in size, shape, and color, is cut from paper or cardboard. Circles or squares may be used, but designs suitable to the occasion are often better. Each figure is cut into two parts, the cut for any figure being different from that for any other; the cuts should, of course, be irregular, resembling those in a jigsaw puzzle. Each player obtains his partner by finding the person with the piece that matches his own.

24. NAME IT

In this variation, one set consists of actual objects or pictures of objects, and the other set consists of the names of the objects. The players find their partners by matching names and objects. This game provides an opportunity to use objects that players may have difficulty in naming.

25. WHOSE BABY?

Each guest is instructed to bring a picture of himself as an infant or small child. The girls' pictures are distributed at random among the boys, and each boy finds his partner by matching the picture given to him with the proper girl. Later in the evening the boys' pictures can be distributed among the girls.

26. DESCRIPTION PARTNERS

This is a method of obtaining new partners after the players have been paired off by some other method. Each boy writes, on a piece of paper, a description of the girl who is his partner. The descriptions are collected, shuffled, and then redistributed among the boys, with care to see that no boy gets the one he has written himself. Then each boy must find, as his next partner, the girl whose description has been given to him. The stunt may be varied by having each girl write her own description. Often such descriptions are not accurate, but this fact increases the fun as well as the difficulty of the game.

27. SPLIT QUOTATIONS

Familiar quotations, either poetry or prose, are collected and each is copied on two cards, that is, half is copied on each card. It may be necessary to omit capitalization or punctuation in order to give no clue as to which half is the first one. One part of each quotation is given to a boy and the other to a girl, and the halves are matched to determine partners. Only the words are matched, not the shapes or cuts of the cards.

28. SPLIT PAIRS

A list is made in advance of common expressions in which two words are connected by *and*, such as *cup and saucer, bow and arrow, Antony and Cleopatra, Jack and Jill, up and down,* or *to and fro.* Such pairs are sometimes called *affinities.* One word of each pair is written on a card and the other on a second card. The cards are then distributed so that one word of each pair goes to a girl and the other to a boy. The players find their partners by matching the words and completing the pairs.

29. SPLIT SIMILES

This is the same as Split Pairs except that the expressions that are split and distributed are common similes, such as *strong as an ox, red as a beet, dead as a doornail.*

30. SPLIT PROVERBS

Well-known proverbs are divided and distributed as in Split Pairs, and each player finds the person with the other half proverb that matches his own.

31. DEFINITIONS AND WORDS

A number of words are written on one set of cards, one word to a card, and their definitions on another set. The cards are distributed and matched for partners, as in Split Pairs.

32. RIDDLE PARTNERS

Riddles are written on one set of cards and their answers on another set. The riddles are distributed among the girls and the answers among the boys, or *vice versa*. Each player must find the riddle or answer that corresponds to his own. (Collections of riddles will be found in Chapters 9 and 20.)

33. STATE-CAPITAL PARTNERS

Names of states are distributed among the girls and names of their capitals among the boys, or *vice versa*. States and capitals are matched for partners. If preferred, outlines of the states may be used, pairing them with either the names of the states or the capitals.

34. AUTHOR PARTNERS

Names of books are distributed among the girls and names of their authors among the boys, or *vice versa*. Players obtain partners by pairing the books and their authors. Of course, the writings need not be confined to books, but might also include poems, essays, or plays. The same idea can be applied to such combinations as pictures and artists.

GROUP B: OBTAIN PARTNERS BY CHANCE

Although the matching method of obtaining partners, just described, depends on chance in the distribution of the things to be matched, the chance distribution is followed by a search for the matching object, statement, or idea. It is through this search that the player finally obtains his partner. The present group is different in that the player draws by lot the actual name of his partner or, for that matter, actually draws the partner in the flesh.

35. COBWEB PARTNERS

Lengths of string are intertwined about a room in such a way that no one can tell one piece from another. The strings go over, under, and around pieces of furniture, and cross and recross one another. One end of each string is given to a girl and the other to a boy. Each player, boy or girl, untangles his string and winds it up into a ball, until he and his partner meet.

36. FISH-POND PARTNERS

Strings or ribbons are thrown over a curtain rod or other horizontal support at a height above the head. A girl grasps one end of each string and a boy the other end. They all pull, and the ones who pull the same string become partners. Some care is needed to insure that the two ends of the same string cannot be identified and that the end for girls will not be confused with that for boys. The surest way to do this is to have a curtain hanging from the rod, but this should not be necessary.

37. GRAB-BAG PARTNERS

Each boy brings a small favor or trinket, wrapped in such a way as to conceal its nature, with his name marked inside the package. Each girl draws one of the favors from a grab-bag and has its owner for her partner. The usual method is for the girls to draw blindly from a bag in which all articles are concealed, but they may be permitted to select packages at will if the nature of the various articles is properly concealed. In a variation, each girl provides an article of personal adornment, such as a bracelet, a ring, an artificial flower, or a handkerchief. (These articles are not given to the boys, but are returned to their owners.) Each boy selects one of the articles and has its owner for his partner.

38. LUNCH-BOX PARTNERS

At a party where refreshments are served, refreshments for two may be placed in a box in which a girl's name has been concealed. Boys select boxes at random, and each eats refreshments with the girl whose name is in his box. When the girls supply the refreshments, each girl places her name in the box that she brings, but the method is equally good when refreshments are provided by the host or by a committee.

39. BALL-OF-YARN PARTNERS

A ball of yarn is unwound and then rewound. As it is rewound, slips of paper are attached at regular intervals, each slip containing the name of a boy. The last of the slips should be inserted some distance from the end of the ball of yarn, so that the later names are covered by the yarn and cannot be identified. The girls stand or sit in a circle and unroll the ball of yarn as they pass it from one to the next. Each girl unwinds yarn until she comes to a name, this name being that of her partner.

40. MARCHING PARTNERS

Two concentric circles are formed, boys in one and girls in the other. The two circles march in opposite directions, to music if possible. When the music stops, or a substitute signal is given, all halt in place, and each takes as a partner the one beside him in the other circle.

41. TALL-AND-SHORT PARTNERS

The boys form a line in order of height, the tallest at the right. The girls form a line opposite them, with the tall girls at the left. The two lines march toward each other until they meet, each person taking as a partner the one that he meets.

GROUP C: OBTAIN PARTNERS BY CHOICE OR GUESS

In the devices for obtaining partners described in Groups A and B, no player has any choice of partners; the outcome is determined entirely by chance. In the methods included in Group C, the player has a choice. In most cases the right of choice is likely to be of little help, but at least he has a chance to guess; in a few cases he has more than a pure guess, and in one case an entirely free choice.

42. PROGRAM CARDS

Each player is given a card with a list of numbers, one number for each of the games or activities of the proposed program. The boys then circulate among the girls, and each boy signs up one of the girls for each of the numbers. The girls do not approach the boys, but record the boys' names on their programs. As an event is announced, each boy claims as his partner the girl with whom he has made an engagement for that number. Sometimes the kind of event is known in advance, but it is usually preferable to have the engagements made without knowledge of the nature of the activities. This method is used occasionally at dances.

43. SHADOW PARTNERS

A sheet is hung in the room and a light arranged so that shadows of the players are thrown on the sheet. The girls stand on the light side with their shadows on the sheet, and the boys on the other side. Each boy selects a partner from the shadows. Of course, positions may be reversed so that the girls select the boys.

44. FOOT PARTNERS

The girls sit behind a sheet or curtain, each extending one foot, without a shoe, forward under the sheet. Each boy selects a foot, and its owner becomes his partner. Both feet can be used, but because shoes can be identified easily, it is best not to wear them. The game can, of course, be used for selection of boys by the girls.

45. HAND PARTNERS

This is the same as Foot Partners except that a hand, rather than a foot, is thrust forward under the curtain.

46. EYE PARTNERS

The girls stand behind a sheet or curtain in which holes have been cut so that only the eyes are visible. Each boy selects a pair of eyes.

47. CINDERELLA'S SLIPPER

Each girl removes one shoe, and the shoes are mixed up in a pile. Each boy selects a shoe and then finds its owner for his partner. This mixer is similar to Matching Shoes (Number 21) except that the boys are permitted to choose the shoes.

48. BALLOON PARTNERS

Two concentric circles are formed, boys in one and girls in the other. Each girl has an inflated toy balloon marked with her name. The two circles march in opposite directions, preferably to music. When the music stops, or a substitute signal is given, all marchers halt and the girls throw their balloons into the air. Each boy grabs a balloon and takes as a partner the girl whose name it bears.

49. CLAP IN AND CLAP OUT

This traditional game, often played on its own account, is basically a method of obtaining partners. Chairs are arranged in a circle, one chair for each boy, and a girl stands behind each chair. The boys gather in a separate room and each one draws a number. The girls also draw the same numbers, so that each girl has the number of one of the boys. One boy is called into the girls' room and his number is called out. He sits down in one of the chairs, hoping to select the chair of the girl who has drawn his number. If he does select this chair, he remains seated. But if he does not, then all the girls clap vigorously, thus forcing him to leave that chair and try another. The moving by the boy and the clapping by the girls continue until the boy finds the right chair. Then the next boy is called in and the same procedure is repeated until all are seated.

Chapter 2

NONCOMPETITIVE GAMES

THE ACTIVITIES DESCRIBED IN THIS CHAPTER ARE GAMES ONLY IN THE broad sense of the word. In a narrower sense, they are not games, because in none of them is there any winning or losing, scoring, or definite objectives; that is, no objectives except to act cleverly and to develop ludicrous situations.

Section I: Consequences games

The distinguishing feature of all consequences games is this: Words, or occasionally phrases or sentences, are selected in advance, with no knowledge of the context into which they are to be fitted. Then a story is told, questions are asked, or statements are made, and the preselected words or sentences are inserted at designated places. In one variation, each player contributes a bit of drawing instead of a word. The result is, of course, a lot of nonsense, but the nonsense is often very amusing. Except when supplying the original words or ideas that are to be used later, the player has no choice; he is required to insert whatever word he has at hand, so that the process is entirely automatic.

GROUP A: COMPLETE A STORY

1. ROMANTIC CONSEQUENCES

This is the traditional game that is referred to when the name *consequences* is used without qualification. The players, except the leader, sit in a circle, and each is given a sheet of paper and a pencil. The paper may have the items below typed on it, but usually they are read aloud by the leader. At the direction of the leader, each player writes in the first space on his paper an adjective applicable to a girl. He then folds the paper so that his writing cannot be seen and passes it to the next player. Then each player writes a girl's name on the paper that has been handed to him, folds the paper again, and hands it to the next player. This process is repeated until each player has written one of each of the items, all on different papers. The complete list of items, or "questions" follows:

1. An adjective applicable to a girl
2. A girl's name
3. An adjective applicable to a boy
4. A boy's name
5. Where they met
6. What she did
7. What he did
8. What she said
9. What he said
10. The consequences
11. What the world said

The list of items may be varied somewhat, but in the traditional game it is well standardized. Naturally, when filling the blanks, the players will not be serious but as clever or as funny as possible. In any case, a ludicrous combination is sure to result.

When the papers are completed, they are read one at a time, either all by the leader or each by a different player. The reader inserts the obvious words needed for continuity, and makes the whole into a story. A story might come out something like this:

> The catty Josephine Brown and the elephantine George Jones met at the West Side Marching and Chowder Club. She dived into the pool from the high board. He ate the last of the sandwiches. She said, "How do you stop this thing?" He said, "All is not gold that glitters." The consequences were that they missed the boat. The world said, "A barking dog never bites."

2. BIOGRAPHIES

Each player is given a sheet of paper. He is instructed to write his name at the top of the paper and the numbers 1 to 20 inclusive down the left margin. Then he is directed to write the following in the twenty spaces:

1. Any year not earlier than 1800
2. Any city or country
3. A whole number not greater than 25
4. Another city or country

5. Either *Yes* or *No*
6. A whole number not greater than 25
7. An occupation
8. Any number
9. Another number
10. A number under 50
11. A color
12. Another color
13. A part of the face
14. A bad habit
15. A sport or hobby
16. A flower
17. A kind of food
18. A number under 1000
19. Any number

When the papers are completed they are collected, and the leader reads a "biography" of each player by using the statements written by the player to fill the blanks in the following:

Mr. John Doe was born in (1) in (2). At the age of (3) he moved to (4), where he now lives. He is married (or not married) (5) and has (6) children. His profession is (7). He earns (8) dollars a year and spends (9) dollars a year. His shoes are size (10). His hair is (11) and his eyes are (12). His most attractive feature is his (13). His worst vice is (14). His hobby is (15). His favorite flower is (16) and his favorite food is (17). He is expected to live to the age of (18) and his heirs will inherit (19) dollars.

3. LAST WILL AND TESTAMENT

Each player is given a sheet of paper. At the top of the sheet he writes "The Last Will and Testament of...." Then he writes the numbers 1 to 12 inclusive down the left margin and inserts his own name in the first space. Having done this, he folds the paper so that his writing cannot be seen, and passes it on to the next player. The second player writes, in the second space, the name of a person of the sex opposite that of the first writer; this person is to make the will jointly with the first writer. The paper is again folded and passed, until twelve players in all have written on it. Each of the twelve from the third through the eleventh does the same thing: He writes the name of any possession, either real or imaginary, that is to be included in the will. Finally the twelfth person, upon receiving the folded paper, writes the name of the person who is to inherit all the things mentioned. Then, of course, the papers are unfolded and the wills are read.

The above describes the game as traditionally played. A simpler, more modern form, which may be better for some situations, has only five spaces to be filled in and names only one article to be bequeathed. The successive writers fill in the spaces as follows:

1. Name of the person making the will
2. Name of any one thing to be bequeathed
3. Name of person to inherit the bequeathed possession
4. Purpose of, or reason for, the bequest
5. A condition applying to the bequest

The will then will read:

> (1) hereby wills and bequeaths (2) to (3) for the purpose of (or in order that) (4); on condition that (5).

4. CONFESSIONS

This game requires three leaders, selected in advance. One leader goes to each player in turn and whispers to him the name of another person with whom he is supposed to be. The second leader goes to each in turn and whispers to him a place or situation—this might be an actual city or country or it might be a situation, such as *on the roof* or *in a tree*. The third leader whispers to each a statement as to what he and his companion are supposed to be doing. The three leaders work independently, each with no knowledge of what the other two are saying. Each player in turn stands and announces what he has been told; for example: "I am Jennie Reed; I am with Bob Hope at a wrestling match, washing dishes."

GROUP B: ANSWER QUESTIONS

5. PREDICAMENTS AND REMEDIES

Players sit in a circle. Each writes on a slip of paper, "What would you do if . . .?" completing his question by naming a predicament of some sort. On a separate slip of paper each player writes what he would do in the predicament. He then passes the predicament to his right, and the remedy to his left, so that each player has two entirely unrelated slips, one describing a predicament, the other giving the remedy for a different predicament. Then one player reads his predicament and the one on his left reads the remedy given to him. The result will be such nonsense as: "What would you do if you ran out of gas on a bridge?" "I would apply a mustard plaster."

Although the principle is always the same, this game is sometimes organized in different ways. Sometimes the players are in two groups, a predicament group and a remedy group, and the predicaments and remedies are passed from one to another in the same group. This requires a player to name a remedy without having any predicament to which it refers, and he is likely to find that this taxes his imagination. In the method described, a player can think of an actual predicament and of a more-or-less logical remedy for it and still, by mixing up the two, produce absurd combinations.

6. SILLY ANSWERS

By one device or another, each player is given a question, and an answer to an entirely unrelated question. In turn, each player reads his question and then his answer, a combination that is likely to be very amusing. There are several ways of selecting and distributing the questions and answers. The best method is for a leader to find, in advance, genuine questions and answers from printed lists; they must be on a variety of topics. He writes each question on a slip and each answer on a different slip. Then the questions are mixed up in one container, the answers in another, and each player draws one slip from each of the two containers. A second method is for each player to write any question on a slip of paper and its answer on another slip, the slips being mixed and drawn as before. Still a third method is for two leaders, working independently, to whisper a question and an answer to each player; that is, one leader gives the questions and the other the answers. When this last method is used, it is common practice to divide the players into two groups, one with questions only, the other with answers only.

7. WHY AND BECAUSE

This game is a special form of Silly Answers. Each question must begin with "Why" and each answer must begin with "Because."

GROUP C: OTHER CONSEQUENCES GAMES

8. GOING TO NEWPORT

With the players seated in a circle, the leader announces that they are all going to Newport, and then says, "I am going to Newport and will take my _____." Here he names dog, airplane, bushel of potatoes, or anything at all, that he intends to take with him. The second player immediately continues, "I am going to Newport and will take my _____," naming anything else. All the others players, in turn, repeat the statement, each naming something different that he will take with him to Newport. When the first round has been completed, the first player begins the second round, this time telling what he will do with whatever he intends to take. If it is a dog he might say, "I am going to wash my dog." The other players in turn repeat the same sentence, except that each substitutes for *dog* the name of the thing that he mentioned in the first round. Thus, the statements might include, "I am going to wash my bushel of potatoes," "I am going to wash my pound of caviar," and so on. When the second round is finished, the third begins, this time with the second player. He tells of something appropriate that he intends to do with whatever he has said he will take, and the others repeat his statement, each of course, substituting his own article for that named by the player who began the round. The game continues until each player has begun a round.

9. WHAT IS MY THOUGHT LIKE?

Players sit in a circle. One of them thinks of some object, person, or abstraction, without revealing it to the others. He then says to them, "What is my thought like?" Each of the other players in turn must answer, his answer, of course, being made entirely in the dark. After all have answered, the first player now says, "I was thinking of _____; why is _____ like _____?" He asks this question of each player in turn, mentioning the thing that person has named. Each must then reply with a statement that indicates some resemblance between the two. For example, the first player may have thought of a baseball game, and some of the replies to his first question may have been, "It is like a man" or "It is like a labor union." In answer to the second question, the player who gave the latter answer might say, "A baseball game is like a labor union because it has many strikes."

10. CRAZY STORIES

The leader selects, in advance, two well-known short stories. Such stories as Jack and the Beanstalk or Little Red Riding Hood are suitable. He cuts up or copies the stories so that each sentence is on a separate slip of paper. After these slips are thoroughly mixed, each player draws one or two of them. Then the players in turn read their sentences, thus producing a nonsensical combination.

11. ART CONSEQUENCES

Each player draws a picture of a man's or a woman's hat on a sheet of paper. He folds the paper so that just enough of his drawing can be seen for the next player to add to it. The second player continues the drawing by inserting the upper part of a face; then he folds the paper in the same way and hands it to the third player. The third player adds the lower part of the face and succeeding players add, in order, neck, shoulders, waist, hips, legs, and feet. The last contributor to each drawing labels it with a name and exhibits it to the group. Of course, the game can be varied so that each drawing is completed in fewer stages than the nine described above.

12. PICTURES AND NAMES

Each player draws a picture on a sheet of paper. Of course, the players need not have any drawing ability; probably the less ability the better. The drawing is handed to the next player, who writes on the sheet a word or phrase as a caption for the picture. Then he folds the paper so that only his words can be seen and hands the paper to the next player. This player must now make a drawing to suit the name that has been handed to him. The fourth player names the drawing of the third, the fifth draws a picture to suit the name given by the fourth, and so on, alternating pictures and names.

Section II: Mindreading and second sight

All the "mindreading" tricks to be described here are much alike: in each there is a mindreader and a confederate; in most cases the confederate's identity is known to all the players, but in others even his existence is a secret. All except the mindreader agree among themselves on some person or object, or possibly some word, number, or idea, for the mindreader to name. By the use of a code or signal, the confederate informs the mindreader of the secret and the latter names it correctly. The tricks differ chiefly in the nature of the code or signal, and it is on this basis that they are classified below.

13. CAHOOTS

One player, the mindreader, turns his back to the group and another player, his confederate, then points to any player and asks, "At whom am I pointing?" The mindreader gives the correct answer.

The mindreader knows that the confederate will point to the player who was the last to speak before the mindreader turned his back. Obviously, both performers must know the identity of the last speaker.

14. THE MAGIC CIRCLE

The mindreader announces that he will leave the room and on his return name the player with whom his confederate has shaken hands during his absence. The mindreader does not leave immediately, but gathers the others around him and goes through some hocus-pocus, chanting something about the magic circle, such as "The magic circle is now formed; do you feel its influence?" After several members of the group have given some reply, he leaves the room and soon returns to identify the person with whom his confederate has shaken hands. He is able to do this because he knows that the person to be identified is the one who spoke first in response to his question about the magic circle.

15. THE SPIRITS MOVE

The mindreader leaves the room but remains within hearing distance. The confederate goes to another player, holds his hands above the latter's head and says, "The spirits move." He does the same with other players at random; finally he says, "The spirits move and rest upon...." Here the confederate pauses, and the mindreader names the player in question. The person to be guessed is the one who was at the right of the confederate as the mindreader left the room.

16. CAR

While the mindreader is absent from the room, the others select one of three objects. The confederate calls the mindreader back, and the latter immediately identifies the object. The signal to the mind-reader is the first letter of the statement used in calling him back to the room: The letter *C* indicates the first of the three objects, *A* the second, and *R* the third. These letters are the initials of the expressions most likely to be used; that is, "Come in," "All right," and "Ready." The idea can be expanded and made more complicated if desired.

GROUP B: CODE IS IN CONFEDERATE'S QUESTIONS

17. NINE BOOKS

Nine books are laid on the floor in a rectangle—three rows of three books each. The others agree on one of the books for the mindreader to identify. A confederate points to the books one at a time, using a yardstick or other pointer. When he points to the selected book, the mindreader identifies it.

The confederate identifies the chosen book by the way in which he points at the first book. Thus, if the chosen book is the one in the center, the confederate points to any book at all, but is sure to point to the *center* of this book. From this point on he can touch the books in any order and ask questions of any kind; the mindreader merely waits for the right book, already knowing which one it is. To give a second example: If the chosen book is in the middle of the bottom row, the confederate first touches any book at all, but touches it at the middle of the bottom; thus the mindreader immediately knows which book has been chosen, and he merely waits for the proper time to identify it.

A clever confederate can make this trick extremely mystifying by giving the impression that he is using some other code. For example, he might point to the first book and say "Is it this?", point to several others with the same question (always emphasizing *this*) and then point to the selected book with the question "Is it *that?*" Some player is sure to think that the code is in the change from *this* to *that* and offer to guess the book next time, only to find that he has been misled.

18. FOUR BOOKS

This trick could very well be used with nine books, but usually only four are used, simply because the code is easier to remember this way. The mindreader undertakes to identify a book that has been selected from a group of four arranged in a rectangle. The confederate points to the books, one at a time, asking questions as he does so, and the mindreader identifies the selected book.

In this case, the code is in the words used by the confederate in asking the first question. For the book on the upper left the question is, "Is it this?"; on the upper right, "Is it that?"; on the lower left, "Is it this one?"; on the lower right, "Is it that one?" As soon as the first question has been asked, the mindreader knows the book to be identified and from this point on the questions are immaterial.

19. FIVE IN A ROW

The mindreader undertakes to identify an object that the others have selected from five placed in a straight line. The confederate points to objects, apparently at random, asking questions as he does so. When he points to the selected object, the mindreader identifies it.

The method is very similar to that used in Nine Books, the object being revealed by the position at which the confederate touches the first object. The code can be varied as desired, but the following is as good as any: touching the first object near the upper left corner indicates the object at the left of the row; upper right, the second object; center, the third object; lower left, the fourth; and lower right, the fifth.

20. TELEPHONE CARD TRICK

This mindreading trick involves difficulties, but when it can be worked it is remarkably effective. The mindreader is absent and unknown, and one of the mystified players is induced to ask the question that contains the code. The players select a playing card from a deck, and one of the group is directed to telephone a certain number, ask for a certain person, and ask this person to identify the card. The person called, after suitable stalling, will name the chosen card.

Of course, the telephone number is authentic, but the name of the person asked for is a fake; this name constitutes the code by which the card is identified. Some person, who cannot be present when the trick is worked, must, of course, be primed to act his part as mindreader and to respond to any name. The name must have a consonant for its first letter and a vowel for its second. The second letter shows the suit of the selected card—*a* for clubs, *e* for diamonds, *i* for hearts, and *o* for spades. The first letter shows the rank—*b* for a two, *c* for a three, *h* for an eight, *l* for a queen, and so on. This system does not work for an ace, a five, or a nine, since such a card would require a name beginning with a double vowel. To get around this difficulty, one might simply decide that an ace, a five, or a nine cannot be used; because this might lead to failure of the trick, it is recommended that the initial letters *n, p,* and *r* be used to indicate the denominations in question, as substitutes for *a, e,* and *i.*

One of the group makes a vague reference to the powers of a friend of his, and the others finally agree to give the mysterious friend a trial. By a method clearly not controlled by the leader, a playing card is selected, say the queen of diamonds. The leader then says to some suitable person, "Call Lawndale 5963 and ask for Dr. Lerner; he will be able to tell you which card has been selected." The call is put through and, after considerable difficulty, "Dr. Lerner" comes to the telephone. He is greatly annoyed at such nonsense, but agrees, rather ungraciously, to name the card. He insists that the questioner have the card in his hand, that he hold it up to the telephone, and so on. Finally he names the card.

21. COUNT THE LETTERS

Four objects are numbered, and one of them is selected by the other players while the mindreader is absent. The mindreader returns, his confederate asks him various questions, and the object is identified.

The selected object is indicated by the number of letters in the first word spoken by the confederate: object number one by a one-letter word, object number two by a two-letter word, and so on.

22. LEGS

While the mindreader is out of the room, the other players select any object in the room, such as a table, a rug, or a lamp. When the mindreader returns, he is asked questions by his confederate and identifies the selected object.

The code is in the first question asked by the confederate, and the mindreader needs only to note whether this question refers to an object with legs. If it does, then the next time the confederate refers to an object with legs, the mindreader will know that this is the one selected. If the first question refers to an object without legs, the selected object will be the next one without legs mentioned by the confederate. For example, if the selected object is a certain chair, the confederate may point to a table and say, "Is it this?" Then he points to a lamp, an ash tray, a book, and various objects, all without legs. Finally he points to the selected chair, thus revealing its identity.

23. CHOOSE A NUMBER

The other players select any number. The confederate calls out various numbers, and when he calls the selected one the mindreader identifies it.

The code is in the first digit of the first number called by the confederate; it shows the place that the selected number will have in the series that he calls. For example, if the first number called by the confederate is 67, then the selected number will be the sixth one called.

The trick can be made more difficult, for both performers and other players, if the confederate, instead of actually calling the selected number, calls this number multiplied by two (or any other multiplier agreed on in advance). For example, for the number 14, the confederate might call: 56, 129, 33, 87, 28. From the first number, 56, the mindreader knows that the fifth number in the series will be twice the selected number, and since the fifth number is 28, the selected one must be 14.

24. BLACK MAGIC

While the mindreader is absent, the other players select any object in the room. He returns, his confederate points to or asks about various objects in the room, and when he mentions the selected object the mindreader identifies it.

The selected object is mentioned by the confederate immediately following the name of any object that is black. Of course, any other color can be used in place of black.

25. LEG MAGIC

This is the same as Black Magic except that the object to be guessed is named first after any object with legs.

26. BOOK MAGIC

Several books are placed in a row, and one of them is chosen for the mindreader to guess. His confederate points to various books, apparently at random, and when he points to the selected one the mindreader identifies it.

The key is that the selected book is always the one immediately following a book at either end of the row. As a variation, it might be agreed that the selected book will follow one that is second from either end.

27. CITY MAGIC

The confederate calls out the names of cities, and when he names the one that the players have selected the mindreader identifies it.

The point is that the confederate always calls the name of the selected city immediately after the first one with a two-word name, such as Los Angeles or New York.

28. RED, WHITE, AND BLUE

This trick is a variation of Black Magic. An object is selected, and the mindreader identifies it in response to his confederate's questioning and pointing. The process is repeated with other objects.

The key: the first object to be identified will be mentioned immediately after any *red* object; but the next time, the selected object is mentioned immediately after a *white* object; and the third time after a *blue* one.

The principle of having a multiple code and changing it for successive objects adds greatly to the effectiveness of mindreading tricks and should always be used when a serious attempt is made to mystify people. Variations of the method are obvious and can be improvised easily. For example, when one object is to be identified from a row of objects (as in Book Magic), it would be simple to agree that the first time the object will be mentioned immediately after one at either end, the second time after the second from either end, and so on.

29. COUNT THE QUESTIONS

A certain number of objects are laid on the floor or table, one of them is selected by the other players, and the mindreader, in answer to his confederate's questions, picks out the chosen object.

The mindreader and his confederate have an understanding by which the objects are numbered, say from left to right. It is immaterial what questions are asked. The mindreader needs only to count the questions and to compare the number of each question with the number of the object to which the question refers. When the two numbers are the same, the chosen object is indicated. For example, if object number five is to be identified, the confederate may ask the first question about number two, the second about number four, but the fifth question must refer to the fifth object.

30. THIS ONE, THAT ONE

In response to his confederate's questions, the mindreader identifies the chosen one from four objects. This trick resembles Four Books (page 24), but the principle is the same as in Count the Questions.

Four different questions are used: "Is it this?," "Is it that?," "Is it this one?," and "Is it that one?." Each of these questions is assigned to one of the four objects, and when a question is referred to the object to which it is assigned, the mindreader knows that object is the chosen one. For example, if the question for object three is "Is it this one?," then the confederate reveals the identity of the object by pointing to it and asking this particular question.

31. TWO ROWS

Two rows of books or other objects are laid on the floor or table, any convenient number in each row. The mindreader answers his confederate's questions and selects an object that has been chosen by the others.

The code is extremely simple, but unusually effective. One of the two rows is designated as the "this" row, the other as the "that" row. The chosen object is indicated whenever the confederate uses the word "this" in referring to an object in the "that" row, or *vice versa*.

It is probably better to use three or four rows of objects. Only the two code words, "this" and "that" are needed, each row being designated by one or the other of these two words.

32. THIS AND THAT

This trick is well known and so simple that it will not fool many people for very long; but it is included here because no collection

would be complete without it. The confederate asks questions, and
the mindreader identifies a selected object when it is mentioned.
The point is simply that the confederate indicates the object by
using the word *that* in asking about it. He will ask, "Is it this?," "Is
it this one?," and so on, but when he asks, "Is it that?" the mindreader knows the answer is "Yes."

GROUP C: CODE IS NOT IN CONFEDERATE'S QUESTIONS

33. SPOON PHOTOGRAPHY

The mindreader claims that a person's image can be transferred
to a bright silver spoon and that, although the picture is not very
clear, it can be recognized by the mindreader. He leaves the room,
and his assistant holds a spoon in front of the face of one of the
players, then places the spoon on the floor. The mindreader returns,
studies the spoon intently, looks the players over, and announces
the name of the one photographed.

The explanation is that the confederate indicates the subject of
the picture by imitating his pose and actions. As the game is usually
played, the confederate is the same as the one who "took the
picture," but it is much better to have the imitating done by a third
person. If the game is played several times, the players are sure to
demand that certain persons act as subjects for the photograph, and
the demands might refer to one of the confederates. It is wise to be
prepared with special signals for this emergency.

34. BLIND VISION

Each player writes a word, a phrase, or a short sentence on a slip
of paper, folds the slip, and deposits it in a container. The mindreader takes one of the slips and, without unfolding it, presses it
against his forehead. He then announces what is on the slip and
asks for the writer to identify himself. One of the players will admit
writing it. The mindreader unfolds the slip and reads it for confirmation; he then goes through the same procedure with the second
slip. He takes the slips one after another and reads them all, simply
by holding each folded slip to his forehead.

The secret is in the method of handling the first slip. The one held
to the mindreader's forehead is an authentic one written by a player
who is not in on the secret; but the words spoken by the mindreader

are not the ones on the slip at all, but rather ones agreed upon in advance with a confederate. In fact, it is not necessary to have a sentence agreed upon, but only an understanding that the confederate will acknowledge authorship of whatever words the mindreader reads first.

When the mindreader looks at the first slip "for confirmation," he is actually learning what is written on it. Then when he holds the second slip to his head and pretends to read it, he actually calls out the words appearing on the first one. He continues thus, always pretending to read the words on a slip but actually calling the words on the preceding one.

If the confederate contributes a slip like everyone else, the mindreader's system will be disrupted when he reaches this slip. It is best for the confederate not to contribute a slip at all. If this method is used, the game will have to be halted before all slips are read; otherwise, the players will notice that one slip is missing. Another possibility, however, is that the confederate's slip be made identifiable and be taken from the container last.

35. TEMPLE READING

A mindreader undertakes to learn, by mental telepathy from his confederate, a certain number that the others have agreed upon. The confederate sits in a chair, and the mindreader places his hands on the cheeks or temples of the confederate. Soon the mindreader announces the correct number.

The confederate keeps his mouth closed and gives signals by tightening his jaws, signals that the mindreader can easily detect with his fingertips. For a small number, the signal is simply the proper number of bites; for a larger one, each digit is indicated by a series of bites, followed by a distinct pause.

This system can be easily adapted to words, a word being spelled out by indicating each letter with a simple code.

36. CARD NAMING

While the mindreader is out of the room, the other players select any playing card from an ordinary deck, then replace the card, and shuffle the deck. The mindreader's confederate places the deck face down on top of a card table and recalls the mindreader, who is able to name the selected card. He names first the color of the card, next its suit, and finally its denomination.

Two different codes are used, the first to indicate the suit of the card, the other its denomination. The confederate indicates the suit of the selected card simply by placing the deck nearest the proper edge of the table, according to a prearranged code—for example, north for clubs, east for diamonds, south for hearts, and west for spades. Therefore, the instant the mindreader sees the deck on the table he knows the suit of the card to be named. He does not, however, name the suit at once, but only its color, and later names the suit; in other words, he uses two statements to say what he could as well have said in one if he had wished to do so.

To each of these two statements the confederate gives a reply to indicate agreement, and it is the nature of these replies that constitutes the code which tells the rank of the card. The confederate must have ready four different expressions of agreement, such as *yes, right, correct,* and *uh-huh.* The denominations are divided into four groups: first group—ace, two, three, and four; second group—five, six, seven, and eight; third group—nine, ten, jack, and queen; fourth group—king only. When the mindreader announces the color of the card, the confederate gives assent with one or the other of the four methods in the code, the one he uses indicating in which one of the four groups of denominations the card is found. Next the mindreader announces the suit (having known it from the beginning) and again the confederate gives assent. In this case, the same set of replies is used as the code, reply number one indicating the lowest of the four cards in a group, reply number two the next lowest, and so on. The mindreader then announces the rank of the card.

Suppose, for example, that the ten of hearts has been chosen. The confederate casually places the deck on the table, somewhat nearer the south edge than any other, and calls the mindreader to the room. The latter observes the location of the deck and, immediately knowing that the card to be named is a heart, announces, "It is a red card." "Correct" says the confederate, thereby indicating that the card is either a nine, a ten, a jack, or a queen. After suitable delay for concentration, the mindreader says, "The card is a heart." The confederate now replies "Right," thereby showing that the card is second-lowest in its group, that is, a ten. It remains only for the mindreader to complete his identification by saying, "It is the ten of hearts." The confederate must, of course, give some reply.

37. THE MYSTIC CANE

As a mystifying trick this one may appear weak, but it has been very successful for many years. Perhaps its popularity is due to the dramatic element and the action included in it. The mindreader tries to guess some simple verb of action that the others have selected, and to indicate the correctness of his guess by acting out the verb. His confederate makes remarks, gives instructions, and taps on the floor with a cane, and soon the mindreader starts to perform the appropriate action.

The selected verb is spelled out by the confederate by means of a very simple code. Each consonant is indicated by using it as the initial letter of the *second* word in a statement, each vowel is indicated by a certain number of taps on the floor with the cane—one tap for *a*, two for *e*, three for *i*, four for *o*, and five for *u*. For example, suppose the selected word is *write*. The confederate might say, "I *w*ish you would all concentrate." Then, after a pause long enough to indicate a new statement, "Get *r*eady now." Then, tap, tap, tap with the cane indicates *i*. Next, "It *t*akes the cooperation of all of you to make this a success," and finally, tap, tap. The mindreader is now ready to take a pencil and paper and begin writing.

38. CIGARETTE MAGIC

The mindreader tries to guess any word selected by the others, and his confederate informs him of the word by use of a code much like the one used in The Mystic Cane. The consonants are indicated in the same way, that is by using them as initials for the second words in sentences. The vowels are indicated by puffs on a cigarette —one puff for *a*, two for *e*, and so on.

39. THE TELLTALE PLATE

The mindreader inverts a plate on a table top and places a coin on the plate. He leaves the room, having given instructions that during his absence one of the players is to remove the coin from the plate and conceal it on his person. He then returns to the room and directs that the players, one at a time, place their right forefingers on the plate. He then names the player with the coin.

The mindreader has a confederate, but this fact must not be known to the other players. The secret is that the confederate is careful to take his turn in touching the plate immediately after the player who has the coin.

Section III: Fortune telling

40. FORTUNE-TELLING CAKE

Various small articles are wrapped in waxed paper and baked within a cake. The articles should be well distributed so that each will go to a different person. When the cake is cut and served, several of the guests will get the articles and from them learn something of their future. The significance of a few of the articles is:

Penny	—poverty
Dime	—wealth
Ring with stone	—first engagement in the group
Wedding ring	—first wedding in the group
Safety pin	—a baby
Heart	—a love affair
Button	—bachelor or old maid

41. FORTUNE HUNTING

Small articles, similar to those used for Fortune-Telling Cake, are wrapped so they cannot be identified, and hidden in various places about the room. The guests search for them, each guest being allowed only one article. These articles reveal something significant about the future of those who find them.

42. FEATHER FORTUNES

Three feathers, one red, one white, and one brown, are placed side by side on a table. Each guest in turn blows the feathers away. The color of the feather that travels farthest indicates the complexion of the blower's future mate.

43. WHO IS BOSS?

All the players are asked to fold their hands at the same time. The leader then announces that anyone who has his left thumb above the right is, or will be, boss in his own home.

44. FOUR SAUCERS

Four saucers are placed on a table, one empty, one containing clear water, one containing milk, and one containing vinegar. A player is blindfolded and instructed to place a finger in one of the saucers, the saucers having been shifted about. The one that he touches first indicates something about his future: water, a happy marriage; milk, wealth; vinegar, poverty; and the empty saucer, that the player will be a bachelor or old maid.

45. THE LOVE APPLE

Each player has an apple and a paring knife. He must pare the apple without breaking the peeling, and then throw the peeling over his shoulder to the floor. The initial most closely approximated by the peeling will be that of the player's future mate. If he breaks the peeling, he will not marry.

46. CROSS-OUT FORTUNES

This game reveals the feeling of one person for another of the opposite sex. The two names are written down, one above the other. Then all letters that are found in both names are crossed out, and the number of letters that remain in each name indicates the feeling of that person toward the other. The remaining letters are counted off in this way: Friendship, love, indifference, hate, friendship, love, indifference, and so on.

Example: WILLIAM JONES
LUCILLE SMITH

Counting the uncancelled letters in William Jones gives friendship, love, indifference, hate, *friendship,* showing that his feeling for Lucille is friendship. The count of the girl's name shows that she has the same feeling for William.

If preferred, only the first name may be used, or the name may be written with a middle initial or complete middle name. Whichever form produces the most pleasing result is the correct one.

Chapter 3

SKITS, GAGS, AND GROUP STUNTS

AMATEUR DRAMATICS, IN WHICH THE PERFORMERS HAVE LINES AND action to learn and rehearse, is not within the scope of this book. Included here are a few stunts and gags of the kind that can be improvised, without preparation of a serious kind, by any reasonably clever players. The chapter includes a very few straight dramatic skits or gags, a few stunts in which all participate, some "contests," and a few fake stunts.

Section I: Straight skits

1. THE PULLMAN PASSENGER

This skit has a cast of three: two pullman passengers and a porter. One of the passengers, a loud and loquacious man, tips the porter well and gives elaborate instructions about getting him out of bed and off the train. He absolutely *must* get up a few minutes before 5 A.M. and *must* get off the train at Podunk at five o'clock. He explains that he will be sleepy, will probably tell the porter that he has changed his mind, and will in every way resist the porter's attempts to get him up. The porter must understand, however, that the man is to be wakened, forced to dress, and put off the train at Podunk. The porter agrees to follow instructions exactly. The next action takes place just before five in the morning. The porter tries to waken the passenger but, as predicted, the latter says it is all a mistake, that he has no desire or intention of getting off at Podunk, that he never heard of Podunk, and so on. But the porter is not deceived. He has been paid to do his duty and he does it. He forces the reluctant passenger out of bed, forces him to dress partly, and shoves him off the train. After the train has left the station, the porter discovers that the man who was to get off at Podunk is still asleep, and that he has forced the wrong man off the train.

2. THE MINDREADER

This is a takeoff on the very common and popular "mindreading" tricks, many of which are described in Chapter 2. As in the straight tricks, the mindreader leaves the room while the other players select some object for him to name. The mindreader returns and his confederate asks questions that enable the mindreader to learn the identity of the chosen object. The point to the skit as described here is that the clues given by the confederate are absurdly obvious, so as to make a joke of the whole thing. For example, if the mindreader is to guess the number four, the accomplice might say something like, "You have just four seconds to answer," or he might make four obvious taps on the floor, and so on. A clever pair can make good fun out of this skit, especially if the group has been participating in some of the straight mindreading tricks.

3. THE ECHO

The fake echo that suddenly becomes independent and stops echoing takes many forms and is always good for a laugh. For instance, a man trying to sell a piece of land hoped to deceive his prospect by claiming that a wonderful echo could be heard from the property. He hired a boy to conceal himself at a distance and imitate an echo of what he heard. At the proper time the seller called "Hello" and echo very properly answered, "Hello." After a few more exchanges the owner called, "Who are you?" whereupon echo replied, "Bill Smith." This gag should not be used in exactly the form described here, but should be adapted to the situation and the people present. It gives an excellent opportunity for clever originality.

4. THE CROOKED-MOUTH FAMILY

This skit requires a cast of five: Pa, whose mouth is twisted to the left; Ma, whose mouth is twisted to the right; their son Bill, whose lower jaw protrudes; their daughter Jane, whose upper jaw protrudes; and their other son Jim, just home from college, whose mouth is perfectly straight. They are all at home when bedtime arrives. Pa is asked to blow out the candle, but he is unable to do so because he can blow only to the left. He calls for assistance from

Ma, but Ma can do no better, because she can blow only to the right. Neither Bill nor Jane, who try in turn, can blow out the candle, for Jane can blow only downward and Bill can blow only upward. At last Jim is persuaded to try, and he blows out the candle with no trouble. Pa remarks, "It shows the value of a college education."

This skit is sometimes done as a monologue, the same person taking all the parts. It is harder than one might think for a person to change rapidly from one crooked mouth to another.

Section II: Group stunts

5. COMMUNITY SNEEZE

The players are divided into three groups. One group is assigned "Hashee," the second "Hishee," and the third "Hoshee." At a signal they all shout at once, each his assigned word. The result is a giant "sneeze."

6. BARNYARD MUSIC

Each player is given the name of a barnyard animal whose call can be imitated. As many animals as possible should be named, but they need not all be different. At a signal the players all give the sounds of their animals as loud as possible.

7. THE FROG POND

The players are divided into three groups, roughly according to voice; that is, the high voices in one group, the middle voices in the second, and the bass voices in the third. The high voices are to say "tomatoes, tomatoes, tomatoes"; the middle voices, "potatoes, potatoes, potatoes"; and the basses, "fried bacon, fried bacon, fried bacon." At a signal all sing at once, each his assigned words.

8. JOHN BROWN'S BABY

To the tune of "Battle Hymn of the Republic," the group sings this song in unison:

> John Brown's baby had a cold upon his chest,
> John Brown's baby had a cold upon his chest,
> John Brown's baby had a cold upon his chest,
> So they rubbed it with camphorated oil.

The song is sung once as given. Then it is sung a second time, but the word *baby* is not spoken. Instead, each singer substitutes a motion of rocking a baby in his arms. Then the whole song is sung for the third time, and motions are substituted for two words—*baby* and *cold*. The motion substituted for *baby* is the same as before, and the one for *cold* is a cough. The next time a third motion is added: a slapping of one's chest as a substitute for the word *chest*. Finally, the motion of holding the nose is substituted for *camphorated oil*.

Thus the song has developed into this:

John Brown's [rocking motion] has a [cough] upon his [slap]
  [Repeat this line twice]
So they rubbed it with [hold nose].

This song is sometimes used as the basis of a competitive game, a player being eliminated when he makes a mistake. It seems better, however, to consider it simply a bit of nonsense for all to enjoy without the competitive element.

9. POST MORTEM

This stunt is gruesome, so much so that it may be upsetting to some people. But for those who can stand it, it is extremely effective. It requires considerable preparation and also some skill on the part of the narrator.

The group sits in a circle in complete darkness. If some light is unavoidable, then the group should sit at a large table and pass the objects under the edge of the table, because the players must on no account see the objects that are passed from one to another. The narrator tells a story, in very sepulchral tones, about a man who was murdered. Various parts of his body have been found, and some of them will be passed around for all to feel. The narrator then refers to the murdered man's brains and as he does so he hands a damp sponge to the next player. The sponge is passed from hand to hand, and the narrator must wait until it has made the complete circuit before he mentions another part of the remains and starts it around. The narrator continues this, starting "parts of the murdered man's remains" around one at a time. Of course, the objects may be varied, but some good ones follow:

Brains: wet sponge
Head: head of cabbage
Ear: dried apple or peach
Hair: yarn or cornsilk
Hand: glove filled with wet sand
Eye: peeled grape
Tongue: raw meat or damp pickle
Heart: piece of liver
Teeth: kernels of corn

Toe: a carrot
Veins: cold cooked macaroni
Windpipe: piece of soft rubber hose
Vertebrae: wooden spools on a string
Tendons: cold cooked macaroni
Rattling bones: clothespins on a string

10. THE STORY OF HARRY

One man tells the story of Harry to another, slapping and mauling his listener as indicated below in parentheses:

> "Oh *Chest*er (slaps him on the chest), have you *'eared* (pulls his ear) about *Hairy* (rumples his hair). He *chest* (slaps him on the chest again) got *back* (whacks him on the back) from the *front* (pokes him in front). They had *kneed* (hits him on the knee) of his *feets* (steps on his feet) in the *arm*y (pulls his arm). *I* (threatens to poke him in the eye), *nose* it; everybody *nose* (pull his nose) it. *Hip, hip* (smacks him twice on the hips), hurray (grabs his arm and waves it overhead)."

Sometimes one person tells the story, performing the gestures or himself. More often, a group is divided into two parts, and one group submits to the punishment by the other; then they reverse. It is most effective when one man simply starts in on another. The listener will usually hold out to the end, not only because he is too surprised to do anything else, but also because he wants to see how the story comes out.

Section III: Fake stunts

11. FAKE ARGUMENT

During a banquet or on some other occasion when someone is giving a speech, a member of the audience rises and takes exception to something the speaker has said. By prearrangement, others enter into the argument, and soon unsuspecting ones join in. The joke must not be allowed to go too far, but should be given away soon. This stunt is very effective if cleverly done, but if not well planned and skillfully carried out, it will fall quite flat.

12. AMBIGUOUS INTRODUCTION

At a banquet, the toastmaster gives an extremely flowery introduction of the next speaker, but he does not give the speaker's name. Instead, he says, "You all know, of course, the man to whom I refer." Thereupon two men rise, each with a prepared speech much in evidence. Each insists that he is the man referred to, and that he has been asked to give a speech. The problem may be solved by the toastmaster's statement that the speaker is neither one of the men, but a third one; in this case, the third man actually gives a speech. Another solution is for each of the two candidates to be allowed to read his speech, one sentence at a time, the two alternating in reading a sentence each. Like the Fake Argument, this stunt will succeed only when well planned and cleverly handled.

13. FAKE GHOST STORY

The performer finds a really good story, one that works up to a very tense climax and, of course, one that is not likely to be known to his audience. He tells the story in an interesting and straightforward manner. When he comes to the point of greatest suspense, he modifies it somehow so as to refer to a drum and then says, "And so they picked up the drum and beat it." Thereupon he walks off and leaves the audience in suspense.

In another, and possibly better, form of this trick, the storyteller works in a reference to a shoemaker. Then he seems puzzled and asks, "What is that thing a shoemaker uses to punch holes in leather?" The answer from various members of the audience will, of course, be "Awl." Then the storyteller says, "Yes, that is all."

Section IV: "Contests"

Included here are a number of "contests" in acting, oratory, or other vocal activity. Although some pretense is made of picking a winner, rather than contests they are more properly considered devices for producing ludicrous situations. As described they are for two contestants only, but most of them can easily be used with larger numbers. Activities of this sort should never be continued for more than thirty seconds, and often shorter periods are better.

14. TALKING CONTEST

Two men are assigned topics—the same topic, two unrelated topics, or the positive and negative sides of a question. A signal is given, and the two men face each other and begin talking. Each must talk fast and continuously; hesitation, even for a second, counts heavily against him. Each must try to make himself heard by the audience. After thirty seconds they are stopped, and the audience selects the winner, on the basis of continuity, eloquence, and audibility. This stunt also works well with three or four contestants.

As a variation, gestures may be absolutely prohibited. In this case, it is better to have four contestants and to determine the winner by a process of elimination.

15. LAUGHING CONTEST

At a signal, two players face each other and laugh as fast and as strenuously as possible for thirty seconds. The audience selects the better laugher.

16. POSING

This is a contest, not in acting, but in assuming poses. Two or more contestants stand with their backs to the audience. The pose is described and they all turn to face the audience and assume the pose immediately. Some poses that may be used are: a girl seeing a mouse; a boy about to take castor oil; a country preacher delivering a sermon; a baseball player protesting a decision.

17. WHISTLING CONTEST

This is the same as Talking Contest or Laughing Contest except that the contestants whistle. Each may whistle anything at all, but he must not stop. The audience selects the winner.

18. WHISTLING FOR ENDURANCE

This is a contest in ability to continue whistling without taking a breath. At a signal, the two (or more) contestants begin to whistle. They may whistle tunes or a single note continuously. A contestant must not take a breath, and his whistle must always be audible to the judges. It is permissible for one contestant to try to make another laugh.

19. SINGING CONTEST

Two contestants sing for thirty seconds, each singing anything he chooses. (If preferred, songs may be assigned.) The audience selects the better singer on the basis of continuity and vigor, not musicianship.

20. BUZZING CONTEST

This is a contest of endurance in making a buzzing sound. Except that the contestants buzz, it is identical with Whistling for Endurance.

21. SOLEMNITY CONTEST

Two contestants stand back to back, and at a signal turn to face each other. They compete to see which can stand longer without laughing. Each man may make any desired motion in an attempt to make the other laugh, but neither must touch the other or make any sound.

Chapter 4

SNARES

A "SNARE" IS A TRAP, IN WHICH AN UNSUSPECTING VICTIM IS CAUGHT. Its success, of course, requires a victim who is ignorant of the hoax and gullible enough to "fall for" it. It also requires the cooperation of any other players who may know the hoax. The snares described here include some in which the victim suffers physical punishment or inconvenience, and others in which he is simply embarrassed or left in an awkward position.

Section I: Physical punishment or discomfort

GROUP A: VICTIM HAS HIS FACE BLACKENED

1. PINCHY WINCHY

All players, including the chosen victim, sit in a circle, the leader at the right of the victim. The players are instructed to watch the leader and listen to him, and to do and say exactly what he does. Then the leader turns to the victim, at his left, pinches him lightly on the cheek and says, "Pinchy Winchy." As instructed, each other player then pinches the one at his left and says, "Pinchy Winchy." The leader then pinches his victim's other cheek, then his chin, his forehead, and so on, each time saying "Pinchy Winchy." Every time each of the others follows his lead with the player at the left. Instead of pinching the victim, the leader may pat him, stroke his cheek with the hand, or make some similar motion. Also, he may vary the words if he desires, saying such things as "Chucky Lucky," "Kootchie Kootchie," or "Skeegee Weegee." Finally, the leader takes a mirror, looks into it, and says, "Pinchy Winchy." The victim, on doing likewise, discovers that his face is marked with numerous spots and streaks of lampblack, which the leader had on his hands.

2. THREADNEEDLE SNARE

The victim is required to thread a needle with one eye closed. This is a good stunt and surprisingly difficult when done with a small-eyed needle. In this snare, however, the victim is given a needle with a large eye so that there is really no difficulty in threading it. He is cautioned sternly that he must keep one eye closed; to make sure that he does so, another player holds one hand firmly over the closed eye. In doing this, he smears lampblack over the victim's eye.

3. THE BLACK SAUCER

This snare is most often used in connection with an initiation into an actual or a fake organization. The victim and the initiator stand face to face and close together. The victim must look the other person squarely in the eyes and not allow his gaze to wander. Then he must make a series of motions in exact imitation of the initiator. Each of the two holds a saucer in one hand, the saucer holding some object to which some significance has been ascribed. With much hocus pocus and with great solemnity, the initiator touches the token in the saucer, touches the saucer in various places, waves his hands in the air, and repeatedly touches his own face, stroking his fingers across his forehead, down his cheeks, and so on. The victim follows every move, but in his case the results are different because the bottom of his saucer has been covered with lampblack. It is not difficult to deceive a victim with this trick. If he keeps his gaze firmly fixed on the eyes of the other man as required, he is not at all likely to discover the lampblack.

4. PHOTOGRAPH

The victim sits for his photograph. The leader, equipped with the necessary genuine equipment, prepares the subject. In doing so, he keeps up a continuous chatter and takes rather unusual pains to pose the victim, turning his head this way and that, elevating his chin and then lowering it again, and so on. All the time the photographer is doing this he is smearing lampblack over the face of the victim.

GROUP B: VICTIM IS PADDLED

5. LIFTING SEVEN MEN

One of the players boasts that he can lift seven men. This leads to considerable discussion, especially among those who know the snare, and finally the boaster is asked to prove that he can do as he says. He lies supine on the floor and then calls for the seven men who are to be lifted. The first six of these men have been carefully instructed as to their positions. Each of them sits on the floor with both legs extended across the body of the lifter, three of them on one side of him and three on the other side. Then the lifter calls for a seventh man—the victim—"to hold the legs down." This man is instructed, and vigorously assisted, to lie face down on top of the legs of the other six, his body being directly above and parallel to that of the lifter. When the victim is in position, or perhaps as he is getting into position, the other six hold him down with their hands and paddle him.

6. WEIGHT GUESSING

One player offers to guess the weights of others and perhaps to pay a penalty if he misses by as much as three pounds. He first takes on a player whose weight he already knows, and who knows the trick. The weigher feels the other's arms and legs, stands back for a good view, carefully estimates height, and the like. Finally, he stands with his back to the player, pulls the player's arms over his shoulders, and lifts him from the floor. He then announces a weight which, of course, turns out to be almost exactly correct. The weigher does the same thing with another player or two, and then takes on the chosen victim. This time the procedure is the same until the victim is lifted from the floor; then all the other players paddle him.

7. WHO HIT ME?

This snare begins, and is played for awhile, as an authentic guessing game. Two volunteers lie side by side on the floor, face down, and are covered with a blanket or sheet. They are to keep their eyes closed so that they cannot see each other or the other players. The blanket is really not necessary, but it helps create atmosphere and adds to the fun. All the other players gather around in a close circle and pass a swatter or paddle about among themselves. One of the players takes a swat at either of those under the blanket and then quickly hands the swatter to another player or throws it to the floor. The one who has been hit throws the blanket off and comes to a sitting position. He looks about and tries to guess which one of the players has hit him. If his guess is incorrect, he resumes his position under the blanket, but if it is correct the one who has swatted him must take his place. After the game has continued for awhile, the wise ones see to it that a preselected victim is correctly guessed as the swatter, and takes his place under the blanket. Now the game changes. From this point on all the swatting, or most of it, is done by the one lying under the blanket with the victim. If the victim is properly fooled, he will always guess that one of the bystanders has hit him; he will, of course, always be wrong. The other man under the blanket should get his normal share of swats to help deceive the victim. If the victim does not catch on in a short time, the game must not be allowed to go on too long. The hoax should be made more and more obvious, so that he cannot help but get the point.

GROUP C: VICTIM IS WETTED

8. DRYING THE FLOOR

This snare requires a floor that will not be damaged by water. A small amount of water is poured on the floor to form a pool. The victim is induced to sit on the floor with his legs spread wide apart, the pool of water between his feet. He is armed with a swatter. Another player approaches with a large towel in his hand and claims that he will be able to wipe up the water with the towel before the victim can hit him with the swatter. Suddenly he grasps the ankles of the victim and slides him forward through the pool of water.

9. FUNNEL TRICK

A boy is selected as victim, and an ordinary kitchen funnel is placed, right side up, inside the front of his trousers; that is, the stem of the funnel is inside the trousers and the mouth of the funnel is outside, above his belt. Then he is told to hold his head well back and balance a penny on his forehead. He is to try to drop the penny from his forehead into the funnel. But, while he is still balancing the penny on his forehead, someone produces a pitcher of water and pours it into the funnel.

GROUP D: VICTIM SUFFERS OTHER PUNISHMENT

10. KNIGHT OF THE BLANKET

This snare, like a number of others, calls for a considerable amount of hocus-pocus and an atmosphere of fake solemnity. It is commonly used as part of an initiation of some sort. Two chairs are placed about two feet apart, and a blanket is draped over them in such a way that it appears a third chair sits between them. Two members of the group sit on the two chairs. After whatever preliminaries seem appropriate, the victim is led toward the chairs and is told to turn around and sit in the middle chair, preparatory to answering certain questions. As the victim sits down, the two who are sitting rise, and the victim tumbles to the floor.

11. I SAW A GHOST

All players stand in a line very close together, with the leader at one end. The leader explains that he is about to tell of the actions of a ghost that he has seen, and that the others are to imitate what he does. He begins, "I saw a ghost and he went like this, Oo-oo-oo." All the others follow with their versions of "Oo-oo-oo." Then the leader says, "He went like this," and flutters his hands, or shakes his shoulders, or makes some other motion. After several such motions, he shows how the ghost got down on one knee, placed one foot forward and raised both arms forward. Finally, the leader says, "He went like this," and pushes the next player so that he falls over sideward. If this is done properly each man will overbalance the one next to him, and the whole row of people will fall over like playing cards.

12. KISS THE MYSTIC BOOK

During a fake initiation the victim is shown "the mystic book." He is told that if he kisses the mystic book three times, he will receive a vision, the gift of youth, or something of the sort. He is blindfolded and allowed to kiss the book once and then a second time. As he prepares to kiss the book a third time, a saucer of flour is placed on the book, and the victim gets a mouthful.

Section II: Awkward position or embarrassment

GROUP A: VICTIM IS IN FAKE DANGER

13. AIRPLANE RIDE

A plank or heavy board at least five feet long is required for this snare. The plank is laid on the floor, or better, on blocks or similar supports just two or three inches high. A victim is blindfolded and persuaded to stand on the plank. Two other players stand upright beside him, and the victim places his hands on their shoulders. Several of the other players are told to take hold of the board and lift it as high as they can. They do, in fact, lift the board but hold it stationary a few inches above the floor, and the two players whose shoulders the victim is grasping gradually stoop as low as possible. It is not difficult to persuade the rider that he is indeed standing on a high place. Then the victim is asked to jump from the board to the floor; if he has been properly fooled, he will be very reluctant to do so.

14. WALKING THE PLANK

A board is placed on the floor, with an obstacle of some sort on the floor just beyond the end of the board. The victim, after being allowed to view the situation, is blindfolded and instructed to walk the length of the board and jump over the obstacle. In fact, the obstacle is removed, and the victim jumps over a nonexistent object. A double-cross can be added to this snare by letting one of the watchers, who believes that he understands the situation, try to walk the plank, this time leaving the obstacle in place.

A pan of water is sometimes used as the obstacle, but only when the floor will not be injured by the water; even then it is not advisable for it can involve considerable danger. A canvas or plastic basin of water would be satisfactory in some situations, but in general it is best to use an empty cardboard box.

15. FAKE OBSTACLE RACE

Objects of various kinds, none more than a foot high, are placed in a straight line on the floor, at intervals of about two feet. Such objects as a pile of books, a woman's old hat, a dishpan, or a football might be used. The victim is placed at one end of the row and told to walk over the course with his eyes open, stepping over each article. Then he is blindfolded and told to do it again. This time all the obstacles have been quietly removed so that the hurdler steps over only imaginary objects. Like Walking the Plank, this snare can be used with the double-cross. After the blindfolded victim has been over the course, and before he is let in on the secret, another player is allowed to try it. He assumes, of course, that all obstacles have been removed, but actually a few of them have been put back in place.

16. WATER TRICK

This trick is played by a single person on a group. The performer partly fills a bucket with confetti or rice. Then he places a dipper partly filled with water in the bucket on top of the confetti. The bucket must, of course, be prepared and handled without letting the group know what is in it; they are to assume that it contains water. If confetti is used, the dipper must be dry on the outside, for otherwise confetti will adhere to it and give the secret away. Having made his arrangements, the performer stands before the group with the bucket on a table and, with a suitable background of hocus-pocus, decides that he needs a drink of water. He lifts the dipper to his mouth and takes a drink. He decides, and loudly declares, that the water is not fit to drink. In fact he is so angered by the poor water that he dashes to the floor the water that remains in the dipper; then he lifts the bucket and throws its contents out and into the faces of his audience.

Group B: Victim is Left in an Awkward Situation

17. HOLD IT A MOMENT

A player partly fills a heavy tumbler or small bowl with water and then boasts that he can make it stick to the ceiling without any support. Standing on a stepladder or stool, he places the upright bowl against the ceiling and holds it there with a yardstick. Then in an offhand manner, he beckons to one of the other players and says to him, "Here, hold it a moment while I get down from this stool." When the victim has taken the stick, the performer gets down from the stool, carries the stool away, and leaves the victim to figure out for himself how to get out of this awkward situation. Of course, he must be relieved before he decides that the only way out is to let the bowl drop.

18. TUMBLER TUMBLING

Someone offers to illustrate that it is difficult for a person to give attention to two things at the same time. A victim is selected and told to extend both hands forward, palms down. A tumbler of water is placed on each of them, and then he is instructed to recite, without error, "Mary had a little lamb," or some equally familiar rhyme. The victim will demonstrate that he is able to do the two things at once and to do both quite well, but soon it will dawn on him that he is not able to get rid of the tumblers.

19. HOLD THE EGG

The leader challenges anyone to hold an egg between his first and second fingers for fifteen seconds without dropping it. When a victim accepts the challenge, he is instructed to extend two fingers through the space at the hinge of an open door, and the egg is then placed between the two extended figures. The leader counts off the fifteen seconds and then all walk off and leave the victim. For obvious reasons, it is best to use a hard-boiled egg.

20. THE TENACIOUS DIME

The leader wets a dime and presses it firmly against the forehead of any player; he then directs this player to shake the dime off. The dime will stick with surprising tenacity, but the player will be able to shake it off with little difficulty, after several shakes. A few other players do the same thing, but when the victim's turn comes, the leader presses the dime firmly against his forehead and then removes it. If this is done with even moderate skill, the victim will have no idea that the dime is not still on his head. When he tries to shake the dime off, he does so in vain, and will require some time to see what is going on.

This snare is sometimes used for fortune-telling. The player is told that the number of shakes required to dislodge the dime will answer certain questions. For some questions, such as the number of years before he will be married, the number of shakes can constitute a direct answer; for others, a code can be used, such as an even number for Yes and an odd number for No. The final question must be one that can be answered by a number, for example, "How many children will you have?" Because the dime has been removed, the answer will be a large number.

21. SHAKE A LEG

All the players sit in a circle. Before the victim is present, one of the women doubles one leg up under her and replaces it with a stuffed stocking, with a shoe on the foot. The victim is assigned the seat at the left of the woman with the fake leg. The leader, sitting in the circle, directs that all others do as he does, and then begins to make all sorts of movements. He pats the back of the person on his right, shakes hands with the one at his left, and so on, making all the motions quite vigorous. Finally he stoops to his right, grasps the ankle of the woman sitting there, and shakes it violently. If all goes as planned, the victim will grasp the fake leg and shake it off.

GROUP C: VICTIM IS EMBARRASSED BY WORDS OR SOUNDS

22. ROYAL ORDER OF SIAM

This old favorite is best with three or four victims at the same time (but not more). The victims, as part of the initiation into the Royal Order of Siam, are required to learn and repeat certain Siamese words. Following directions, they kneel in a row and extend both arms overhead. They bend forward and place both palms flat on the floor in front, repeating as they do so the Siamese words "O wha." Then they rise to the original kneeling position with arms overhead saying, as they rise, "Tah nah." They bow forward a second time, saying the word "Siam." Following the leader, they go through these motions several times, with gradually increasing speed, and continue until each one discovers that he has been saying, "Oh, what an ass I am."

23. WHAT AM I DOING?

The victim is instructed to repeat the question "What am I doing?" thirteen times without taking a breath. He is led to believe that he will have difficulty in asking the question so many times without a breath, but in fact finds it rather easy. When he has finished the leader answers his question by saying, "Making a fool of yourself."

24. CHINESE PRAYER

The victims are instructed to kneel on both knees, bend forward, and place their foreheads on the floor. While they retain this position, the following words are called out by the leader, one line at a time, and are to be repeated by the kneeling players in the same way:

> I know my heart,
> I know my mind,
> I know that I'm
> Stuck up behind.

25. CONSTANTINOPLE

The victim is directed to spell *Constantinople,* spelling and pronouncing one syllable at a time. He begins, "C-o-n, con; s-t-a-n, stan; t-i, ti." At this point, all the other players break in, shouting "No!" The victim believes he has made an error and begins again, but each time he says "ti," the others shout "No." Finally, he realizes that they are merely announcing the next syllable.

26. BARNYARD MUSIC—SNARE FORM

This is the snare form of the group stunt described on page 38. Each player is secretly assigned a barnyard animal to imitate. A variety of animals should be assigned, but they need not all be different. One of the players, or more if preferred, is assigned the donkey. It is explained that a signal will be given and that all, in unison, are to imitate their animals as loudly as possible. When the signal is given, all except the victim remain silent, allowing the one player to make a donkey of himself.

27. GUREZ

A player is asked to pronounce J-u-a-r-e-z. This is, of course, the name of a Mexican (also Argentinian) city and is pronounced "hwä′rās." Presumably the player will answer correctly. Then he is asked to pronounce G-u-r-e-z. As he tries various answers, such as "Guray," the leader continues to repeat "G-u-r-e-z." Finally, the player realizes that the other is actually saying, "Gee, you are easy."

28. FAKE TELEPATHY

A victim is selected to try his powers of telepathy. While he is out of the room, the others select some object for him to identify. When he returns to the room, the others are instructed to concentrate on the chosen object in an attempt to reveal its identity to the victim through telepathy. The victim tries hard to read the minds of the others and guesses an object. His guess is incorrect, and he tries again. This time no matter what object he names he is told that he has guessed correctly. He tries again and again, and never fails to name the object on the second try. Of course, the other players never really select an object at all, and the victim never actually makes a correct guess. However, he is heartily congratulated on his extraordinary powers and is likely to have some difficulty in realizing that he has been duped.

29. FAKE TEMPLE-READING

A leader leaves the room while the others select any number not greater than ten. The leader returns and places his fingers on the temples of the players, one after another, in an effort to learn the selected number. The players are to try *not* to reveal the number, but it is explained that some of them will probably do so in spite of themselves. In fact, one of the players, who is a confederate of the leader, actually reveals the number by contracting his biting muscles the appropriate number of times. The leader counts the number of bites to determine the number. This part is the same as in the standard mindreading game (see page 31).

When the leader learns the number, he proceeds as if nothing had happened, until he comes to the victim. After feeling the victim's temples, he concentrates closely and then announces the number, claiming to have learned it from the victim.

30. I AM A GOLD LOCK

This snare and the two that follow are similar. They are very simple and so obvious that one who falls into the trap is likely to do so voluntarily; but they are very old and traditionally popular among children. One child announces that he will make a series of statements, each including the word *lock*, and that a second child is to repeat each statement but substitute *key* for *lock*. The dialog then goes like this:

First child	Second child
I am a gold lock.	I am a gold key.
I am a brass lock.	I am a brass key.
I am a tin lock.	I am a tin key.

After as many such exchanges as the first child desires, the dialog ends thus:

I am a monk lock.   I am a monk key (monkey).

31. JUST LIKE ME

One child announces that he will make a series of statements and that a second child is to respond to each one with "Just like me." The dialog then goes:

First child	Second child
I went up a pair of stairs.	Just like me.
I went up two pairs of stairs.	Just like me.
I went into a room.	Just like me.
I looked out a window.	Just like me.
And there I saw a monkey.	Just like me.

32. OLD DEAD HORSE

In this inelegant little game, two children are to alternate in repeating a statement that is the same each time except that a number, which is included in the statement, is increased by one at each repetition. The first child says, "I saw an old dead horse; I one it." The second child replies, "I two it." The first child says, "I three it"; the second replies "I four it." This continues until the second child is called upon to say "I eight it."

33. BOOTS WITHOUT SHOES

The victim is told to say "boots without shoes." The leader repeats this instruction several times, varying the emphasis and the tone of his voice to mislead the victim. If the snare is successful, the victim will continue to say "boots without shoes," until he catches on that he is to say simply "boots," without saying "shoes." The same trick could be worked with "taxation without representation," "peaches without cream," or any similar phrase.

34. WHOM YOU LOVE BEST

This snare is best with some build-up, as in a mock initiation. In any case, the victim should be asked several harmless questions, to which he can readily give proper answers. Finally, he is told, "Say whom you love best." At this point, it is hoped that he will name some person, or at least think that he is expected to name one and be embarrassed. After his confusion has continued for a suitable time, it is explained to him that he is expected simply to repeat the words "whom you love best."

35. JAW ACHES

The victim is asked to pronounce "j-a, w-a, c-h-e-s." He is likely to say "jay wachees" or something of the sort, but the correct reply, of course, is "jaw aches."

36. PRONOUNCE MAC

The victim is asked to pronounce several words that begin with *Mac*, for example, MacDougal, then MacLeod, then MacHenry. Finally, he is asked to pronounce "M-a-c, h-i-n-e-r-y." He is very likely to say "MacHinery" or something of the sort, thinking it a proper name, but he will soon learn that the proper pronunciation is that of the common word *machinery*.

37. PRONOUNCE TO

The victim is asked to pronounce "t-o," then "t-o-o," and then "t-w-o." He will, of course, give the correct reply in each case, but the questioner must listen very closely, ask for repetitions, and inquire, for example, whether the victim intends to pronounce all three words in precisely the same way. Finally, the victim is asked to pronounce "the second day of the week." He will probably pronounce "Tuesday," only to be informed that the second day of the week is Monday.

38. REBUS SNARE

The victim is asked to read the following rebus:

$$\frac{\text{John}}{\text{Ton}} \qquad \frac{\text{Wood}}{\text{Sam}} \qquad 7 + 6 = 13 \qquad \text{Limburger cheese}$$

This is, for the most part, a standard rebus (see Chapter 18) that can be read easily by anyone who knows anything at all about rebuses. Probably the victim can read "John Overton" and "Sam Underwood" and "sum"; if not, he should be assisted with these items. But he will probably not be able to make a complete sentence. He learns that the rebus is to be read, "John Overton sent Sam Underwood some Limburger cheese." He is sure to ask, "But where do you get the *sent?*" He is then told "from the Limburger cheese."

39. FOUR QUESTIONS WRONG

A proposes to ask four questions of *B* and predicts that *B* will be unable to answer all four *incorrectly*. *A* then asks three questions and presumably receives appropriately incorrect answers. *A* pauses for reflection and asks, "Let's see, that's three questions, isn't it?" If *B* answers "Yes," as he is likely to do, then *A*'s prediction proves correct.

Chapter 5

ORAL WORD GAMES

MOST WORD GAMES ARE PLAYED WITH PAPER AND PENCIL; SUCH games are described in Chapter 9. This chapter includes only those in which words are spoken, although some of them can also be played as writing games. The games in this chapter are divided into two classes, those in which words are spelled, and those in which words are called out.

Section 1: Oral spelling games

1. SPELLING BEE

The players are divided into two equal teams, and each team stands, or sits, in a line facing the other. To ensure that he takes his proper turn, each member of a team should be directly opposite one on the opposing team. From a list of words prepared in advance a neutral leader calls out a word to be spelled. The first speller is the person at the designated end of team A, and the second speller is the member of team B directly opposite him. The third speller is number two of team A, the fourth is number two of team B, and so on, the order zigzagging from one end to the other. When the last player of team B has had his turn, the same order is repeated without interruption.

If a player spells his word correctly, the next player is given a new word; if he spells it incorrectly, the next player tries *the same word*. This word is repeated until someone spells it correctly.

After a player misses the spelling of a word, there are several procedures that may be followed. One is to eliminate the one who has failed, requiring him to leave the game entirely and sit on the sidelines as a spectator. When this method is used, the game continued until one team has been completely eliminated.

58

With another method, players are eliminated for failure, but only a predetermined number of rounds are played, the winning team being the one with the larger number of survivors when the rounds are completed. Probably the best method of all is to have no elimination but to keep all players in the game and simply compare the numbers of words missed. In this case, of course, the number of words or rounds must be decided in advance.

The words for a Spelling Bee must be selected with considerable care. It is customary and proper to begin with relatively easy words and to go on to more difficult ones, but the advance must not be tediously slow. Before the game has been played too long, rather difficult words—but familiar ones, not rare or highly technical,—should be used. Words such as *embarrass, inoculate, innuendo,* and *repellent* will keep most spelling bees from lasting too long, and it is only in a most unusual situation that words like *edulcorate* and *opisthognathous* can be justified.

2. SPELLDOWN

Spelldown is the same as Spelling Bee except that it is played without teams. All players stand in a single line and spell in order from the right end of the line to the left an indefinite number of times. There are two common forms of the game. In one form, a player who fails is eliminated from the game, which continues until only the winner remains. In the other form, a player who fails moves to the foot of the line and spells again when his turn comes in his new position. This form is continued as long as desired, each player, of course, trying to reach the head of the line and remain there.

3. RIGHT-OR-WRONG SPELLING BEE

As in Spelling Bee, two teams face each other, and players spell in the same order as in that game. When a player has spelled a word, the opponent whose turn comes next must immediately call either "Right" or "Wrong." The leader then gives the correct spelling if necessary, and if the player who has just called is in error he scores a miss exactly as if he had misspelled a word. Thus either of the two players can miss on a single word, or both can miss, and no word is ever spelled by more than one player. The one who has called "Right" or "Wrong" is given the next word to spell.

4. BACKWARD SPELLDOWN

All players sit in a circle. The leader calls words and the players take turns in trying to spell them backward. Players may be eliminated for failure, but it is better to keep them all in the game and keep track of the score. Words for this game should be easy ones; it is really not so much a test of spelling ability as of the ability to call the letters in an unusual order.

5. SPELLING BASEBALL

The players are on two teams, each with a definite "batting order." The leader calls a word, and the first batter tries to spell it; if he succeeds he goes to an imaginary first base, but if he fails he is out. The leader then "pitches" a word to the next batter *on the same team* and continues until three men have been put out. Then the opposing team comes to bat. The only way for a base-runner to advance is to be forced by a succeeding batter and, since all hits are singles, four correctly spelled words are required for a run. Obviously, the words for this game must be difficult enough to put three men out within a reasonable time.

6. GHOST

Players are all seated in a circle. One of them starts the game by thinking of any word of more than three letters and calling out the first letter of that word. The next player must think of a word of at least four letters beginning with the first player's letter, and he calls out his second letter. Each player in turn must think of a word that begins with the letters already called, and he must call one additional letter but—and here is the most important rule of the game—he must never complete any word. For example, the first player might think of *apple* and call "a." Suppose the second player thinks of *agriculture;* in this case he calls "g." The third player thinks of the word *against* and calls "a." The next player might think of *again* and call "i." The one who follows him may be unable to think of any words except *again* and *against.* For either of these words he must add *n* and thus complete a word.

The game takes its name from the method used in scoring. When a player is forced to complete a word, he becomes "a third of a ghost." When he loses a second time, he becomes two-thirds of a ghost, and the third time a whole ghost. A whole ghost suffers whatever penalty may be provided.

Often, either from ignorance of correct spelling or by plan, a player will add a letter without having a legitimate word in mind. Whenever one is suspected of doing this, any other player may challenge him; whichever player loses the challenge has a third of a ghost added to his score.

Another important feature of the game is this: A player who has not yet missed, and hence is no fraction of a ghost, is not permitted to speak to any one who is a fractional ghost; if he does so he becomes a third of a ghost himself. This means, of course, that the fractional ghosts will do their best to elicit remarks from the other players.

Even in an informal game, there should be a clear understanding as to what kinds of words will be accepted, and it is very wise to have a dictionary handy. It is probably best to prohibit all capitalized words, and all words of two or three letters should be disregarded.

7. FORE-AND-AFT GHOST

This game is the same as Ghost with the very important exception that a new letter may be added either to the beginning or to the end of the letters already called.

Section II: Word-calling games

8. INITIAL CALL

All players but one sit in a circle, the odd one standing in the center. A category—flowers, cities, famous people, or anything at all —is announced or agreed upon. The odd man calls out any letter of the alphabet, and the first circle player must respond promptly with a word in the category that begins with the letter called. As long as the responses are acceptable, the center man calls letters one after another, and the circle players call the words in regular order. When a response is incorrect or too slow, the one at fault trades places with the odd man. The category may be changed as often as desired. The term *promptly* can hardly be defined, but a group will have little difficulty in deciding doubtful cases.

This game, and others like it, can be played with cards about six inches square, each one showing a single large letter of the alphabet. The center man shuffles the cards, picks one at random, and flashes it instead of calling a letter.

9. INITIAL-CALL RACE

One player, the leader, stands in front of the others, who sit in a semicircle. A category is announced or agreed upon, and the leader calls or flashes a letter. Each of the players tries to be the first to call a word in the category beginning with the given letter, and the first to do so scores a point. This game is especially good with alphabet cards because the score can be kept by giving the card to the player who is first to call.

10. LAST AND FIRST

A category is agreed upon—rivers, cities, trees, or the like. The first player calls any word at all in the category. The player next to him must then call a second word in the same category beginning with the final letter of the first word. The third player names a word that begins with the final letter of the second word, and so on until a player fails to name a correct word or repeats a word that has already been called.

11. WORD LIGHTNING

The leader points to any player and calls a letter. The player begins calling words beginning with that letter—any words at all except proper names. He continues calling words as fast as he can for one minute, and the number of words is counted by the others. This process is repeated with different players as often as desired, and scores are compared. The calling of the words is astonishingly difficult, and the number called in a minute is sure to be much smaller than expected. Word Lightning is best when considered an informal stunt rather than a competitive game. If the scores are to be seriously compared, the leader must be aware of the difference in frequency of the letters; he must also take care to rule out duplicate words and to count the words accurately.

12. SNIP

All players but one sit in a circle, the odd man in the center. The center man points to any man in the circle, pronounces and spells any three-letter word, counts to twelve, and calls "Snip." For example, he says, "Cat, C-A-T, 1-2-3-4-5-6-7-8-9-10-11-12, Snip." Before the center man can finish, the one pointed to must call out three words that begin with the three letters of the word called. Thus, in the example given, he might call "Coffin, Atlanta, take." Any word at all is acceptable, provided that it begins with the proper letter and is named in its proper order. When a circle man fails, he trades places with the center man.

13. TRAVELER

One man stands in the center of a circle formed by the other players. The center man points to any circle man and says that he is going to a certain place, for example, "I am going to Pittsburgh." The one pointed to must, within five seconds, call out three nouns all beginning with the initial letter of the place mentioned. Thus, in the example given, he might say, "pear, pie, pandemonium." When a circle man fails, he trades places with the center man.

14. THE MINISTER'S CAT

All players sit in a circle. One of them begins the game by saying, "The minister's cat is an _____ cat," inserting any adjective beginning with *a*, such as *avaricious*. The next player repeats the statement exactly, except that he uses a different adjective beginning with *a*. Each player in turn must repeat the statement with a new adjective, all adjectives beginning with *a*, no repetition being permitted. This continues until some player is unable to name an adjective that begins with *a*, or repeats one that has already been used. About five seconds should be allowed each player. When a player fails, he has a point scored against him and starts the next inning, this time with adjectives beginning with *b*. The player who fails on *b* begins a series with *c*, and so on, until it is time for a new game.

15. YOU HAVE A FACE

Players are all seated in a circle. One player turns to the next and says, "You have a face." The one addressed asks, "What kind of face?" and the first player answers "A _____ face," using any adjective at all. The same dialog is repeated between the second and third players except, of course, that a different adjective is used;

this adjective must have the same initial letter as the first one. The dialog is repeated until someone fails, each new player naming a new adjective that begins with the same letter as the first one. The one who fails has a point scored against him and begins a new series by naming an adjective that begins with any letter.

16. CATEGORY ALPHABET

Players sit in a circle. One of them begins the game by naming any category and calling any word in the category. Each other player in turn calls a new word in that category beginning with the same letter as the first word. When a player fails to give a proper word within five seconds, he has a point scored against him and begins a new series by naming a new category and calling a word.

17. I LOVE MY LOVE

All players sit in a circle, and one of them begins by saying, "I love my love with an A, because he is _____," naming any adjective that begins with *a*, such as *adorable* or *angelic*. The second player says, "I love my love with a B, because he is _____," naming an adjective that begins with *b*. The game continues until a player fails to name an adjective beginning with the next letter of the alphabet. He has a point scored against him and begins a new series with *a*.

Another form of the game requires each player to name three words, all beginning with the same letter. The formula is, "I love my love with an A because he is _____. His name is _____ and he lives in _____."

18. I LOVE MY LOVE—VARIATION

This game is the same as the one above, except that all players call words beginning with the same initial. For example, if the first player says, "I love my love with an S because he is sweet," the next might say, "I love my love with an S, because she is saucy"; the third might say, "I love my love with an S because he is sensible," and so on.

19. I WENT TO THE MARKET

This game is much like I Love My Love, except that it requires naming nouns instead of adjectives. For example, the first player might say, "I went to the market and bought apples." The second player repeats the statement, except that he buys something that begins with *b*; the third, something that begins with *c*, and so on, until a player misses.

20. ALPHABETICAL ADVERBS

The first player mentions a person (usually one of those present), an activity attributed to that person, and an adverb that might apply to the activity—the adverb beginning with the letter *a*. He might, for example, say, "Bill Jones plays golf *atrociously*." Each player in turn repeats the same statement, except that he substitutes an adverb that begins with the next letter of the alphabet, so that Bill might play golf *beautifully*, then *conscientiously*, *divinely*, *easily*, and so on, until some player fails.

21. A WAS AN APPLE PIE

This game requires naming verbs in alphabetical order. The first player begins, "A was an apple pie. A *ate* it." The second player substitutes a verb that begins with *b*; the third, a verb that begins with *c*, and so on. The statement, "A was an apple pie" is not repeated. The game might go like this: "A was an apple pie. A *ate* it," "B *baked* it," "C *cut* it," "D *designed* it," and so on.

22. INITIAL ANSWERS

The player are seated in a circle, and one of them asks any appropriate question of the group in general. This question must be answered by all the other players in turn, and each player must give an answer that consists of two words with the same initials as his own first and last names. For example, if the first question were, "What is your hobby?" George Smith might reply, "Gathering snakes," and Betty Jones might say, "Baking jellyroll." When a player fails to give an acceptable answer in five seconds, he loses a point and asks the next question.

If preferred, the reply can consist of three words, the words beginning with the player's three initials.

23. ALPHABET TRAVELING

The players are seated in a circle. The first one begins the game by turning to the second and saying, "Where are you going?" The second player replies by naming any place at all—country, city, or town. Then the first player asks, "What will you do there?" and the second must reply in two words, both with the same initial as the place to which he is traveling. For example, the dialog between *A* and *B* might go like this: *A*: "Where are you going?" *B*: "To France." *A*: "What will you do there?" *B*: "Fry fireflies." Then *B* asks *C*, "Where are you going?" and the process is repeated. The dialog continues around the circle until some player misses, each player naming a place with an initial not used before. Sometimes the game is played with three-word replies.

Chapter 6

GAMES OF ALERTNESS AND SELF-CONTROL

In the games of this chapter, a player must make, or refrain from making, prescribed responses to signals or situations. In some of the games, he is required to avoid the normal response and to make an arbitrarily prescribed one instead. In other games, he makes a normal response, but must be prepared to make any of several different ones. In still other games, the problem is to refrain from making the normal response—that of laughing.

Section I: Forbidden-word games

1. NO-VOWEL SPELLING BEE

A spelling bee is conducted in the usual way, on either a team or an individual basis, except that some very special rules apply to the method of spelling words. No player is permitted to pronounce any vowel, but for each one must substitute a prescribed motion. Instead of pronouncing the letter *a*, he raises his right hand; for *e*, he raises the left hand; for *i*, he points to one of his eyes; for *o* he points to his mouth, and for *u*, he points to any other player. A player fails if he pronounces a vowel, if he gives an incorrect substitute for a vowel, or if he misspells a word. The game may be varied by adding *s* to the forbidden letters, the substitute for it being an audible whistle.

2. ACTION SPELLING

This game is very similar to the No-Vowel Spelling Bee, but the prohibited letters and the substitutes for them are different. The prohibited letters are *a*, *r*, and *s*. The substitute for *a* is a wave of the right hand; for *r*, a wave of the left hand; and for *s*, a whistle. The prohibited letters and their substitutes can be changed easily, and players should experiment with various ones. Some possibilities are a wink for the letter *i*, shading the eyes for *c*, growling for *g*, and hissing for *s*.

3. BUZZ

Players are seated in a circle. One of them calls "One," the player at his left calls "Two," the next one "Three," and so on indefinitely, the numbers being called in order around and around the circle. *But*, no number can be named if it is seven, any number containing the digit 7, or any multiple of seven. When a player is due to call a number that is a multiple of seven, he calls the word "Buzz" instead; if it is a number that includes the digit 7, then "Buzz" is substituted for the 7, and the rest of the number is pronounced as usual. For example, 17 is "BUZZteen," and 73 is "BUZZ three," whereas 67 is "sixty BUZZ." Thus, the first numbers are: one, two, three, four, five, six, BUZZ, eight, nine, ten, eleven, twelve, thirteen, BUZZ, fifteen, sixteen, BUZZteen, eighteen, nineteen, twenty, BUZZ.

4. FIZZ

This game is similar to Buzz, except that the forbidden number is five instead of seven, and the substitute word is "Fizz" instead of "Buzz."

5. FIZZ-BUZZ

This game combines the requirements of Buzz with those of Fizz. That is, a player must call "Buzz" whenever he would do so in the game of Buzz, and the word "Fizz" whenever he would do so in the game of Fizz. Thus, fifty-seven is FIZZ-BUZZ, seventy-five is BUZZ-FIZZ, and thirty-five could be either BUZZ-FIZZ or FIZZ-BUZZ.

Section II: Games of ready response

6. BOBBY-DE-BOB

One player stands inside a circle formed by the others. Each player has a number, all numbers being greater than fifty. The center man moves about and at short intervals points to various circle players. Usually, when he points to a player he calls "Bobby-de-Bob," and the one pointed to must call out his own number. Occasionally, the center man will use some other words or point without saying anything. If a circle player makes any response at all when the center man has not called the specified words, or if he makes a slow or incorrect response, he trades places with the center man.

7. PIPPETY-POP

All the players but one stand or sit in a circle, with the odd man in the center. The center man suddenly points to the players, one after another, calling out in each case either "Pippety-pop" or "Poppety-pip." The one pointed to must respond instantly, his response to the first-named call being "Pip" and to the second, "Pop." A circle player who gives a slow or incorrect response must trade places with the center man.

8. CROSS QUESTIONS

The players sit in two parallel rows, facing each other. One player walks around behind the rows, occasionally moving from one to the other, and addresses questions at players in the farther row, that is, the row of players who are facing him at the moment. Each question must be clearly directed at one particular player, the player usually being called by name. But the one to whom the question is directed must disregard it entirely, and the player opposite him, in the other row, must answer the question. Whoever answers when he should not, or hesitates when he should answer, becomes the new questioner.

9. BEAST, BIRD, OR FISH

All players but one stand or sit in a circle, with the odd man in the center. The center man has a soft ball of some sort, perhaps one of crumpled paper. As unexpectedly as possible, he throws the ball at one of the circle players, calling as he does so, "Beast, bird, or fish—Bird," or "Beast, bird, or fish—Beast," or "Beast, bird or fish—Fish," and immediately counts to ten. The one at whom the ball has been thrown must mention an animal in the category named before the center man completes his count; also, he must not repeat a word that has already been used. If the circle man succeeds, he trades places with the center man; otherwise, the center man tries another player.

The speed of the center man's statement and his count is important, and should be adjusted in the light of experience; if it is as rapid as possible without interfering with perfectly distinct enunciation, it will be about right. The first few players should have little difficulty, but it is surprising how soon the rule against duplication catches up with them.

10. EARTH, AIR, FIRE, AND WATER

Players form a circle with the odd man in the center. The odd man tosses a soft ball at one of them, exactly as in Beast, Bird, or Fish. As he tosses the object he calls one of these words: *earth, air, fire, water.* Before the odd man counts to ten, the person to whom the object has been tossed must make an appropriate response: for *earth* an animal that walks, for *air* one that flies, for *water* one that swims; and when the call is *fire* he must remain completely silent. One who makes an incorrect response trades places with the center man.

11. THE PRINCE OF PARIS

The players form a circle, and each is assigned a number. One of them begins the game by saying, "The Prince of Paris has lost his hat. Have you found it, Number five, Sir?" (Of course, any other number could be called.) This statement begins a dialog betwen Number one and Number five, which continues thus: *Five:* "Who Sir, I Sir?" *One:* "Yes Sir, you Sir." *Five:* "No Sir, not I Sir." *One:* "Who then Sir?" *Five:* "Number nine (for example) Sir."

Number nine must jump to his feet immediately and say, "Who Sir, I Sir?" and then he and Number five go through the same dialog, ending with the calling of a new number by Number nine. This continues until a player makes an error in the dialog, or until one fails to jump to his feet immediately when his number is called. The one who fails starts a new game.

12. HICKEY-PICKEY-HOKEY-POKEY

This is a game of quick response that is valuable in perfecting the players' familiarity with each other's names. All players except one sit in a circle. The odd man stands in the center, points to any circle player, and calls "Right (or left), Hickey-pickey-hokey-pokey." The one pointed to must call out the name of the player next to him, on the side called, before the center man finishes his call. The first player to fail trades places with the center man. The circle players must be rearranged frequently.

13. NUMBER-CALLING

All players sit in a circle. The chairs are numbered consecutively, and each player takes the number of the chair in which he sits, his number changing when he moves from one chair to another. Number one starts the game by calling any other player's number thus: "One calling six." Six must immediately respond by calling another number, such as "Six calling nine," and nine by calling another, and so on. The game goes on indefinitely until someone makes a mistake by responding out of turn, calling a number not assigned, or hesitating too long. The one who makes a mistake moves down to the chair with the highest number, and the ones below his old chair move up one space, all who move taking the numbers of their new chairs for the next series of calls.

Section III: No-laugh games

14. LAUGHING BALL

One player stands a short distance in front of the others, who form a straight line or, better, a semicircle. The odd man has a rubber ball that he throws into the air and then catches, either as it descends or after one or more bounces from the floor. All the other players are required to laugh vigorously while the ball is out of the thrower's hands, but to be perfectly silent before he throws it and after he catches it. Anyone who laughs at the wrong time is eliminated, and the process is repeated until only one player remains. The game can easily be adapted to team scoring. A handkerchief may be thrown instead of a ball, the laughing to cease when the handkerchief falls to the floor.

15. SOBER CONTEST

Players form two teams, and each team stands in a straight line facing the other. Team A is allowed a specified time (about forty-five seconds) to make the members of team B laugh. Any member of team B who laughs must immediately withdraw, and every man who does so counts one point against his team. Then the teams reverse their roles, and team B has forty-five seconds in which to make the members of team A laugh. The winning team is the one that eliminates the larger number of opponents.

16. LAUGHING BLACK-AND-WHITE

This game is so named because it includes some of the elements of the well-known tag game called "Black and White." A nonplaying leader has a piece of board about four inches square, colored white on one side and black on the other. The teams, one designated *Black* and the other *White*, stand in two parallel lines facing each other. The leader stands between the teams and tosses the board upward so that it turns end over end and falls to the floor. When the board comes to rest on the floor, the team whose color corresponds to that on the board must become completely solemn and remain so until the next toss, while the other team may laugh at will. Any player who laughs while his team's color is up has committed a foul and must pay whatever penalty has been decided upon. The most common procedure is that of requiring the player at fault to become a member of the opposing team, the game to continue until all are on one side. This method seems quite unsound, but it is widely used and somehow appears to work in many games. Another method is simply that of counting the players who laugh at the wrong time and comparing the scores.

17. HA HA HA

All players sit in a circle. One player calls "Ha," the one at his left calls "Ha Ha," the next "Ha ha ha," and so on, each one adding a "Ha." All this must be done with a perfectly straight face, and anyone who laughs or smiles or fails to produce the proper number of "ha's" has a point scored against him.

18. POOR PUSSY

This is a silly little game that has been very popular for a long time. It is usually played by mixed groups, but it has been used very successfully with groups of only one sex. All players sit in a circle. A boy leaves his place in the circle, stands in front of one of the girls, kneels before her and cries, in as catlike a tone as possible, "Meow." The girl then strokes or pats the top of his head, saying, "Poor Pussy." This dialog, with its action, is repeated and then repeated a second time; that is, the boy, without getting up from his kneeling position, calls "Meow" three times, and each time the girl responds with "Poor Pussy." The object of the game is for the boy to make the girl laugh or smile, without doing so himself. If he succeeds in doing this, he takes his seat, and the girl then kneels before some other boy and calls "Meow." If the boy laughs or smiles before the girl does, he tries again with a different girl.

Chapter 7

ORAL GUESSING GAMES

THIS CHAPTER INCLUDES GAMES IN WHICH PLAYERS TRY TO GUESS objects, words, or ideas that have been selected by the other players. In a few of the games, the guesser has little or nothing to go on, but must guess at random. In most cases, however, he is given clues or has a chance to ask questions giving him considerable opportunity for logical deduction. The games are grouped on the basis of the kind of information or hints that are available to the guesser.

Section I: Question-and-conversation guessing games

In this group of games, a player bases his guesses on statements made by the others. In most cases, these statements are answers to questions posed by the guesser; usually such answers are restricted to "Yes" or "No," so that the guesser must depend on his own skill in selecting questions. In other cases, the answers are not so restricted, whereas in still others, there are no questions at all but only remarks made by the players.

1. TWENTY QUESTIONS

One player thinks of an object. It must be an actual concrete object, not a class of things or an abstraction, and must, of course, be something that the other players can reasonably be expected to know about. The others then ask questions of the one who has selected the object, always questions that can be answered "Yes," or "No," or "I don't know." The guessers are allowed not more than twenty questions. If one of them makes a correct guess without exceeding the allotted twenty questions, he then selects the next object to be guessed; if no one makes a correct guess, the same man selects another object, after revealing the first one. The questioners should take regular turns, except when one thinks he has the answer; he may ask at any time, "Is it . . .?" Such a question always counts as one of the twenty.

The game may be varied so that the first question is "Is it animal, vegetable, or mineral?" This question is answered always directly. However, if the one who has selected the object tells in advance whether it is animal, vegetable, or mineral, the players are allowed one extra question.

2. REVERSE TWENTY QUESTIONS

This game is the same as Twenty Questions, except that the object to be guessed is selected by all players but one; only one player asks questions and tries to guess the object. He asks questions of the others in turn and, of course, must guess the right answer in not more than twenty questions.

3. YES OR NO

This game is almost the same as Twenty Questions, except that: (a) The object to be guessed must be in a prescribed category; (b) The number of questions, although sometimes limited to twenty, is usually unrestricted.

Although this game and Twenty Questions are almost identical in form, they are different in spirit. In Twenty Questions the object to be guessed should be familiar to every player, and it is against the spirit of the game to select an object, or to ask a question, that requires any particular knowledge. The game is a test of deductive ability. In Yes or No there is more leeway in selecting the thing to be guessed; it might be a Bible character, a species of tree or bird, a book title or author, and so on. Both asking and answering questions calls for some knowledge in the field of the item to be guessed. This game is especially good as a teaching device and is often used in nature study. When a question is answered by "I don't know," it should not be counted. Yes or No can also be played like Reverse Twenty Questions.

4. WHAT AM I?

Except for the method of asking and answering questions, this game is really the same as Yes or No. One player selects a person or an object in a prescribed category—literary character, movie star, animal, tree, and so forth. He then assumes the identity of the thing to be guessed, and questions are asked and answered accordingly. For example, questions might be, "Do you have compound leaves?" or "Do you live in the United States?"

5. TEAM TWENTY QUESTIONS

This is the game of Twenty Questions adapted to team competition. Players are divided into two teams, and each team sends out one man to oppose the other team. The two men agree on a secret object or person. Each team plays an ordinary game of Twenty Questions in an attempt to learn the secret from the man who has been sent to them by the opposing team. The two teams should not be able to overhear each other. The team that learns the secret in the fewer questions wins a point; if neither team learns it after twenty questions, neither side wins. After a round is finished, the two men return to their teams, and two others are sent out. The game continues until every man has had a turn at opposing the other team. The team that wins most of the rounds is the winner.

6. WHERE AM I?

One player imagines that he is in some specific place, doing some definite thing. The other players, in turn, ask questions in an attempt to learn where he is and what he is doing. All questions must be answered by "Yes," "No," or "I don't know." The first member of a team to get the complete answer is next odd man. However, if no one on the team guesses the answer in a specified time, the odd man wins. There is no restriction as to the place or the activity that may be selected, except that the players must be familiar with them. A player might be "in the Library of Congress, playing a game of ice-hockey," or "in my bed at home, playing the piano."

7. WHO AM I?

Each player has pinned on his back a sheet of paper on which is written the name of a well-known person—living or dead, real or fictional. His object is to find out the name on the paper. To do so, he asks each of the other players one question only, a question that can be answered "Yes," "No," or "I don't know." Then each player questioned in turn directs a question at the other. In short, each of the two men asks the other a question. When a player has learned the name on his placard, he removes it but remains in the game to answer questions until all have learned their names.

8. MURDER

One player is appointed to take the part of a murderer, another to be his victim. Neither of them knows who the other is, and no one else in the group knows anything at all about the appointments or the game to be played. At an opportune moment, the lights are turned out, the murderer "stabs" his victim, and the victim falls to the floor with a piercing scream. After a few seconds, the leader has the lights turned on, calls the group together, and appoints a player to act as detective. The one appointed tries to find out who did the deed. He may question any of the survivors, and all except the murderer are required to tell the complete truth. The murderer may lie as much as he dares to, remembering that being caught in a lie may convict him. It must be emphasized that the victim does not know when to expect the attack nor who his attacker will be, and that the other players are not aware that a "murder" is to take place.

9. TEAKETTLE

All players but one agree on a set of two or more homophonic words, that is, words that have the same sound but different meanings, such as *so, sew, sow,* or *pain, pane.* The odd player tries to guess the homonyms. The others talk among themselves and to the odd man, always including the idea of the selected word in one or more of its meanings. They never actually speak the word, but always substitute for it the word *teakettle.* Thus, if *sew, so, sow* were the chosen words, one player might say to another, "I find it *teakettle* difficult to *teakettle* that stiff material, don't you?" The other might reply, "Yes, especially since my back is sore from *teakettleing* grass seed all afternoon." The conversation should be free and easy and not allowed to lag. Remarks should be addressed to the odd man, and he may even be allowed to enter the conversation. When the odd man learns the words, the one whose remark has given them away becomes the next guesser

10. THROWING LIGHT

Two players select a word for the others to guess. It is permissible for them to select a set of homophonic words as in Teakettle. The two converse with each other, loud enough for all to hear, making repeated reference to the chosen word but not actually using it. Thus, if *dog* were the chosen word, they might remark, "Mine keeps me awake at night," "I wish I had a spotted one," "Do you find the upkeep expensive?" When a player believes he knows the word he does not say so, but simply enters the conversation by making a statement, or asking a question, that will indicate he has guessed the word. A player must not speak at all until he is ready to indicate he knows the word. When he does so, and has been accepted by the original pair, he continues as a member of the discussion group. The game goes on until all players are talking.

11. GOSSIP

While one player is out of the room, each of the others writes a statement about him. Naturally, the statements tend to be humorous, but they must have some application, truthful or ironical, to the absent player. The written statements are collected, the player is recalled to the room, and the statements are read to him. He tries to identify the authors of the statements, and the first one correctly identified takes his place for a repetition of the game. Whether the statements are to be compliments or slams may be specified before the game is begun.

12. COMPARE IT TO ME

While one player is out of the room, the others choose some object in plain sight. The odd player returns and goes up to the others in turn, saying to each one, "Compare it to me." The one addressed must, by some truthful or fanciful statement, indicate some similarity between the object and the odd player. Answers may be farfetched, but not pointless. Naturally, some players will make very clever comparisons, and others will not do so well. When the guesser has identified the object, the one to make the last comparison replaces him for the next round. For example, if a metal paper knife were chosen, it might be said to be like the player in question because it is smooth, hard as nails, a handy thing to have around, and so on. It is best not to specify that each statement must be a compliment or a slam because this rule will interfere with the cleverness of the comparisons.

13. PREDICAMENTS

One player leaves the room while the others select some predicament, such as "Out of gas on a lonely road," or "Lost in the jungle." The odd man returns and tries to learn the nature of the predicament. To do so he asks the players in turn, "What would you do?" and each must give an appropriate answer. The one who gives the predicament away is next odd man.

14. GUESSING PROVERBS

One player leaves the room while the others agree on a well-known proverb for him to guess. The odd man returns and asks questions of the others in turn. Each one addressed must answer the question put to him, and his reply must include one word of the selected proverb, the words coming in normal order; that is the reply to the first question must include the first word of the proverb, and so on. The one who gives the proverb away is next odd man.

In a variation of this game, no questions are asked, but each player in turn makes some kind of statement, including the proper word of the proverb, as above.

15. RHYMING TOM

The unusual feature of this game is that guessing is done by both sides. One player is against all the others. He thinks of any word and then announces another word with which it rhymes. For example, he might think of *hat* and then say, "I am thinking of a word that rhymes with *sat*." Each player in turn must think of a word that rhymes with *sat* and ask a question about his word without using it. Such questions might include: "Is it used in a game?" "Is it an animal?" "Is it a light blow?" As each of these questions is asked, it is up to the odd man to guess the word to which it refers and to answer the question accordingly. To the examples given he would thus reply, "No, it isn't bat," "No, it isn't cat," "No, it isn't pat." On the other hand, if a player says "Is it worn on the head?" then he must reply, "Yes, it is hat." When a player guesses the original word, or when he asks a question that the odd man cannot answer, he becomes odd man for the next game.

Section II: Dramatic-action guessing games

Group A: Acting is by Opponents of Guesser

16. ACTING CHARADES

The word *charade* is frequently misused. There is more than one kind of charade, but they are all based on the same idea. Any charade is based on a single word, and it must be a word the sound of which can be divided into two or more other words: for example, *intrusion* can be divided into the three words *inn, true,* and *shun, decorate* can be divided into *deck, oar,* and *ate.* By a variety of means—verbal description, picture, or dramatic action—a person or group represents first the component words one at a time and then the entire original word, and other persons try to guess the word. Games or puzzles that treat whole ideas as units are not properly called *charades. Verbal charades,* that is charades in which the clues are given in verse or prose, are classed as puzzles and are not considered here.

In Acting Charades, the players are divided into two equal groups. One group withdraws from the room, agrees on a suitable word, and return to act it out—the first syllable, then the second, then other syllables if any, and finally the whole world. The word *acting* is not to be taken literally; the representation is often merely a pose, or tableau, and it never includes spoken words. After the first group has presented its word, the other group has a reasonable time to consult and decide what the word is. If they guess correctly, they take their turn as actors; if not, the same group presents another word.

In traditional charades, the key word is always divided strictly by syllables, but other kinds of division are often permitted, as the division of *caricature,* into *carry, cat,* and *sure.* It is always permissible, and often preferable, to specify a category in which a word must fall.

17. ADVERBS

One player selects an adverb, and the others try to guess it. Each of them in turn calls upon the odd man to do some specific thing in the manner indicated by his adverb. For example, the odd man might have selected the adverb *swiftly*. He is commanded by the first player to dance "in the manner of the word," and he must then dance swiftly. He then may be called upon to sing, to talk, to walk, to eat, and so on, all in the manner of the word. The first player to guess the adverb becomes the next performer.

Like all guessing games in which one man opposes the group, this one can be varied by having one man try to guess an adverb that has been selected by the others. In this case, each player in turn must perform an act specified by the guesser in the manner of the adverb.

18. ACTING PROVERBS

Players are divided into two groups. One group withdraws, agrees upon a suitable proverb, and comes back to act it out. When the proverb is guessed, the second group selects one and acts it out. Pantomime is most often used, but there is no reason why words should not be used.

19. ACTING NURSERY RHYMES

This game is identical with Acting Proverbs, except that the players act out nursery rhymes instead of proverbs.

20. ACTING TITLES

This is the same as Acting Proverbs, except that the groups act out titles of books, plays, songs, movies, and so on. The category of each title should be announced.

GROUP B: ACTING IS BY TEAMMATES OF GUESSER

This group includes several forms of a single game. This game is one of the most popular parlor games known, so popular that the only name by which it is generally known is simply *The Game*. Although details vary, the essential idea is always the same: one player is given a word, phrase, or title, which he tries to convey to his teammates by pantomime and gestures in less time than that required by an opposing team.

21. PANTOMIME RACE I

As explained above, this game is generally known as *The Game*.
The title Pantomime Race has no standing, but is suggested as a
substitute for the usual name, which is somewhat presumptuous and
perhaps confusing.

The players are divided into two teams. The teams assemble in
separate rooms or as far apart in the same room as possible. Each
team selects a temporary captain to do its acting in the first round
or inning. The leader has selected, in advance, a number of words or
phrases to be dramatized, writing each selection on a slip of paper.
(These items should be familiar ones and not too long. They may
include the names of people, places, or events; titles of songs, books,
paintings, or plays; proverbs, well-known sayings, quotations, and
so on.) When all is ready, he hands a folded slip to one captain and
a duplicate of it to the other; the slips should not be opened by the
captains until a signal is given. When the signal is given, each
captain reads his slip, making sure, of course, that his teammates do
not see it; he then acts out the idea on the slip to enable his teammates to guess the words. The first team to guess the words scores
a point. Then each captain returns to the ranks of his team, a new
captain is appointed, and a second round of the game is played.
The rounds are repeated, with a different captain each time, until
each player has had a turn as captain. Then the scores of the teams
are compared to determine the winner. A time limit of about four
minutes should be set, and any inning declared a draw if neither
team has made a correct guess within that time.

There is some limitation on the dramatic activity of the captain.
He is not permitted to speak or to utter any sound, but may make
almost any gesture or motion. There are a few obvious exceptions.
He may not, for example, make motions that actually indicate the
letters in a word, nor take such an extreme step as looking up a word
in a dictionary and pointing to it. The guessers are free to talk
among themselves and to the captain, and one of the captain's most
important privileges is that of indicating approval or disapproval of
his teammates' guesses, by traditional or arbitrary signs.

Some of the signals to be given by the captain are needed so
frequently that they, and the order in which they are given, have
become standardized to a certain extent. For example, he may first

indicate the number of words in the phrase by holding up the corresponding number of fingers. Second, he will probably try to show the category into which the item falls—by pointing to any man in the group, he may indicate that the word to be guessed is a man's name, or by making the motions of singing indicate that it is a song title. Each time the captain tries to convey a word, his teammates make guesses, and he indicates the right ones by nodding his head.

After the group has learned the category and the number of words, the captain then must try to give further information. He will try to give the most suggestive clue first, or possibly select the one that seems easiest to convey. He may decide to pick out one particular word and dramatize it; in this case, he holds up the appropriate number of fingers and waits for a player to call out, "_____ word." On the other hand, the captain might prefer dramatizing the whole idea as a unit; in this case, he indicates his intention by forming a circle, either with his thumb and forefinger, or with his arms. Another common practice is to work on a single syllable of a word. The captain indicates, as above, the number of the word involved and, after confirming a player's guess, makes a motion of chopping his forearm with the other hand. As soon as a player has called "a syllable of the word," and the captain has confirmed the guess, he holds up fingers to indicate which syllable, and then works on the designated syllable.

The signals described above are the ones most needed and the ones most nearly standardized, but many more will be used. Some are perfectly obvious, such as a "come-on" signal to indicate that a player is on the right track or an expression of disgust to show that he is very far from right. Others will be devised by players as they are needed.

22. PANTOMIME RACE II

In this form of Pantomime Race the two teams do not work simultaneously, but in turn, and the items to be guessed are necessarily different for the two teams. The items may be prepared by the leader in advance and drawn by the teams, but it is customary for each player to write an item on a slip of paper and then for each team to dramatize and to guess the items provided by the other team. Thus one team appoints a captain, who draws an item and dramatizes it until his teammates guess it. The time is noted and then the other team appoints a captain, who draws an item and proceeds as did the first.

The game should be played as first described, if at all possible. It is true that where separate rooms are not available, there is some conflict between the activities of the two teams, and some confusion. However, the players will be so intensely interested in their own game that they will have little desire to profit from overhearing their opponents, and the system is completely workable except where the two teams are very close together.

23. PANTOMIME RELAY

This game is simply the Pantomime Race conducted as a relay. A neutral leader stands at a point midway between the two teams. The teams send their first captains to the leader, who gives them identical words. Each captain rushes back to his own team and proceeds exactly as in the basic game. The first player to guess the complete phrase returns to the leader and gets the second one, then runs back to his team and begins acting. When this phrase is also guessed, a third player runs for another. The game goes on until each player on the team has had a chance to act, no one having more than one turn. The team that finishes first is winner.

24. DOUBLE PANTOMIME RACE

In this variation of the Pantomime Race, the item to be guessed is always a pair of words commonly associated in an expression, or a pair of persons or things associated in thought; for example, "time and tide," "bread and butter," "Adam and Eve," or Robinson Crusoe and Friday, Toscanini and Orchestra, and so forth. Two players always act together. In other respects, the game is the same as the basic one.

25. QUIZ PANTOMIME RACE

This novel game is the Pantomime Relay with a quiz element added. The players form two teams, and the leader, located midway between them, presents identical questions to a captain from each team. Each captain runs to his team and asks the question orally. If any member of the team gives an answer that the captain accepts as correct (the captain has not been told the answer), then any member of the team rushes back to the leader and tells him the answer. If the leader accepts the answer, he hands the player the second question, and this player proceeds exactly as did the first one. As long as each question receives an answer that is accepted by both captain and leader, the race continues as described. If no player can answer the question, the captain must decide whether he can answer it himself. If not, he must run to the leader, who will tell him the answer. Whether he gets the answer from the leader or believes that he knows it himself, he conveys the answer to his team by the method used in Pantomime Race. As soon as a member of his team has discovered the answer, the game proceeds as before, that is, with the next player running to the leader for the next question. Because the provision that the player who answers a question is always the next runner will result in an uneven distribution of the activity, it is recommended that the players of each team take turns.

26. DRAWING RACE

This game begins in the same way as Pantomime Race; that is, the players are divided into two teams separated as far as possible, with a neutral leader midway between them. Each team sends a temporary captain to the leader, and the leader gives the captains identical slips with the word or phrase that their teams are to guess. Each captain runs to his team and gives the clues on which the guesses are to be based. But from this point on the game is different, for the captain may not give the clues in pantomime but only by drawing them on a sheet of paper. The only exception is that he may give nods to indicate approval or disapproval of what his teammates say. He may be allowed to indicate the number of words and their approximate length by drawing dashes. Otherwise, he must do the best he can with his drawing. This game may, of course, be played as a relay.

Section III: Guessing from other hints

27. HANGMAN

This excellent and very popular game is often played by two players, one against the other, but more often by groups, one player selecting the word to be guessed and the others taking turns at guessing. One player draws a picture of a hangman's gallows on a sheet of paper or a blackboard. Then he selects a word in any prescribed category and draws a row of dashes, one for each letter in the word. The other players take turns in guessing the letters of the secret word. naming vowels first, since they are sure to make one correct guess soon.

The first guesser says, perhaps, "Does it have an *a*?" If the secret word does include an *a*, then this letter is written over the proper dash to show its position in the word. However, if the word does not include this letter, a picture of a man's head is drawn in the noose of the gallows. The players continue to make their guesses in turn. After each correct guess, the letter is written in its proper place; after each incorrect one, another part of the man hanging from the gallows is drawn. At the second bad guess his trunk is drawn, at the third and fourth his two arms, and at the fifth and sixth his two legs. If the group guesses the complete word before the man is finished, they win; if not, they are hanged. The number of steps required to finish the hanging is usually six, as described, but in a group that prefers long or difficult words, it is well to increase the number to eight or even more. This can be done by including in the drawing the man's neck, nose, eyes, and so forth, or by including the gallows itself in one or two parts.

28. SHOUTING PROVERBS

Players form two teams, and one team selects a proverb for the other to guess. Each member of the first team is assigned one word of the proverb, the same word being given to more than one player if necessary. At a signal, the members of the first team shout in unison at the tops of their voices, each his own word. The opponents try to guess the proverb and they become the next shouters if they succeed.

29. HOT AND COLD

While one player is out of the room, the others agree on something that he is to do when he returns. The absent one comes back, tries to find out what he is to do, and then actually does it. His only clues are signals from the others indicating whether he is getting closer or farther away from the prescribed action. The simplest method is for the players to call "warm," "hot," "very hot," "cold," "colder," and so on, in the traditional way. Other, and better, methods, include playing a piano or singing with varying degrees of loudness, or turning the volume of a radio up and down. Possibly the best method is for someone to beat on a pan with a big spoon or a stick.

30. DUMB CRAMBO

Players form two teams, and one team agrees on a word for the other to guess; it is often specified that this word be a verb. They then announce a word that rhymes with the chosen one. For example, if they select the word *throw*, they might say, "We want a word that rhymes with *slow*." The guessing team holds a conference and selects several words that rhyme with the one given. They pick out one of these words and represent it in pantomime, presumably with sufficient skill that the other team will know whether the guess is correct. If it is not correct, the other team boos or hisses or otherwise expresses disapproval, and the same team tries again with another word. When a correct guess is made, the spectator team indicates the fact by clapping. Then the two teams reverse roles for the next game.

Section IV: Guessing the game

These games can be played only by a group that includes players who are not familiar with them. They all follow the same pattern: players take turns in doing or saying something, but the uninitiated ones seem unable to do or say the correct thing, although they think they are following the others exactly. Soon a player catches on, but continues to play without interruption. The others catch on one after another, and the game ceases when all are doing the correct thing.

31. THE MOON IS ROUND

The players sit in a circle. The leader asks each of the others in turn to do and say just what he does. Then he leans forward, extends one forefinger to the floor, and draws a big sweeping circle to represent a moon, two dots for the eyes, a vertical line for the nose, and a horizontal line for the mouth. He coordinates these words with his motions: "The moon is round; it has two eyes, a nose and a mouth." The others then take turns in doing, or trying to do, the same thing. Some will know the game and hence will do the right thing, but others will be told that they are not following the leader. The leader is actually drawing with his left hand, a fact that is likely to be missed.

32. HE CAN DO LITTLE

Players are seated in a circle. The leader thumps the floor several times with a cane as he says, "He can do little who can't do this." He then hands the stick to the next player. Each player in turn tries to duplicate the words and actions of the leader. The point is that the cane is held in the left hand and passed to the next player with the left hand.

33. CROSSED AND UNCROSSED

The players are seated in a circle. A pair of scissors is passed from one player to the next, around and around the circle. Each player, as he passes the scissors, says, "I received them uncrossed and pass them uncrossed," or "I received them uncrossed and pass them crossed," or "I received them crossed and pass them uncrossed." He may open and close the scissors at will and pass them either as he received them or not. The words *crossed* and *uncrossed* apparently refer to open and closed scissors, but when used do not have any relation to the actual state of the scissors as passed. Actually, the words *crossed* and *uncrossed* do not apply to the scissors at all, but rather to the feet or legs of the speaker.

34. MY FATHER IS A MERCHANT

The players are seated in a circle. The leader says, "My father is a merchant and he sells shoes [or any other article]." Each player in turn repeats the sentence, naming any article he wishes. Some statements are accepted by the players who know the game, and others are not. The uninitiated finally learn that, for an article to be acceptable, the speaker must be touching it.

35. GRANDMOTHER'S TEA

The players are seated in a circle. The leader says, "My grand-mother likes coffee but she doesn't like tea." This statement is best made with no preliminary explanation at all; the leader just makes it as a casual remark. Perhaps some of those present will know the game, but if not, it will be apparent that each of the others is to make a statement similar to that of the leader. They will say such things as, "My grandmother likes peaches, but she doesn't like cream," or "She likes cabbage but she doesn't like lettuce." (The first of these examples would be rejected, but the other accepted.) Frequently, a player will make an acceptable statement purely by accident, thus adding to the mystery. It finally becomes clear to all that grandmother does not like the letter *T* and hence does not like any food that has this letter in its name. She likes peas, cabbage, okra, bread, and many other things, but she simply cannot stand potatoes, carrots, peanuts, or butter.

36. THE COOK'S PEAS

In this game, the first speaker says, "Our cook likes beans, but he doesn't like peas." The cook does not like anything that contains the letter *P*. The game may be varied to include articles other than food. In fact it is a better game with this variation, since the letter *P* does not work so well with food names as does the letter *T*.

37. I NO

The leader announces that any player who knows the right thing may become a member of the "I know Club." He says, "I know football [for example], and that admits me." Each of the others in turn tells what he knows. If one should say that he knows law, or trees, or carpentry, he would be courteously admitted to the club. But one who claimed to know medicine, or athletics, or agriculture would be refused membership. The players are, of course, to guess what it is that admits some and keeps others out. They eventually learn, perhaps with a few pointed hints, that they must know something the name of which does not contain the letter *i*.

38. GOING TO EUROPE

The leader begins the game by saying, "I'm going to Europe and I'll take ....," mentioning a book, for example. He adds that anyone who takes the right thing may accompany him. Each in turn must say "I'll take ....," and is told either that he can go to Europe or not, depending on what he plans to bring with him. The game continues until all realize that each must take something beginning with the initial letter of his own last name. Thus Mr. Brown can take a book, Miss Perkins can take a purse, and Mrs. Smith can take a sandwich or a samovar.

The game can be modified to require a two-word answer with the initials of the player's two names. Betty Anderson might take a brown anteater and Jim Jones, a jam jar.

39. WHO IS IT?

This game is really quite a fraud, but it has been popular for many years. One player is sent from the room, and when he returns is told that he must guess the identity of another player who has been selected by the group. He asks questions of the others in any order, but may not ask more than one question of any player at any time. All his questions must be answered by "Yes," "No," or "I don't know." The players do not select a particular person, but rather the player at the left of the person answering a question. Thus if the question is "Is it a boy?" the answer may be "Yes" at one time but "No" at another. The game continues until the odd man guesses the point.

This game may be used with players all of whom know the point. In this case, the leader changes the formula for each new guesser, arbitrarily selecting the *third person to the right, the second person to the left,* and so on.

40. MALAGA GRAPES

The players are to observe the leader and to do exactly as he does. He holds a pencil in his hand, taps it on the table or on his knee, and says, "Malaga grapes are very fine grapes, the best grapes in town." The players finally realize that he always clears his throat just before beginning his statement.

41. WILLIE WILLIE

The leader holds up one hand, with fingers extended and spread. Then, with the forefinger of the other hand, he touches the tip of the little finger, then the third, the second, and the first. Next, he makes an exaggerated swoop with the pointing forefinger, down the side of the stationary forefinger and up the side of the thumb. Finally, he touches the four fingers again in order, starting with the first and ending with the little finger. As he does this he says, "Willie, Willie, Willie, Willie, Whoops, Willie, Willie, Willie, Will." The "whoops" comes with the swoop down the forefinger and up the thumb. Other players now try to duplicate the actions and words of the leader. In this case, there are two points that may escape the observation of the other players. For one thing, the stationary hand is always the right, and the pointing finger is the forefinger of the left. Also, as the performer finishes the stunt, he casually folds his hands.

42. THE POINT OF THE GAME

All players but one sit in a circle, the odd man in the center. The odd man is instructed to ask questions of the others in turn, any questions at all, and from their answers to learn "the point of the game." He should be told that personal questions will be most helpful to him. He asks questions of all kinds and gets answers that do nothing but confuse him. Eventually he learns that each person answers questions as if he were the person at his left.

Chapter 8

GAMES OF OBSERVATION AND MEMORY

THIS CHAPTER INCLUDES GAMES BASED ON TESTS OF A PLAYER'S ABILITY to remember what he has seen or heard. In most of these games, the player is aware that he is to be tested later, but in some of them he has no such warning. The chapter also includes games in which a player is required to discover or detect something that is hidden or obscure.

Section I: Observation and recall

1. OBSERVATION

About twenty objects of considerable variety are placed on top of a table and covered with a cloth. The players gather around, and the cloth is removed. After all have studied the objects for one minute, they are again covered. Each player then writes on a sheet of paper a list of the objects that he can remember. Usually, it is required only that each object be mentioned—for example, "a playing card," or "a pencil"—but with more advanced players it may be required that they give colors, denominations, or other descriptive details. Score one point for each object correctly listed, but deduct two points for an object on the list that was not on the table.

This makes a good team game. Players are divided into two teams. All observe the objects as in the standard game, but with the collaboration of its members, each team makes only a single list. The objects should be more numerous for the team game.

2. CHECKERBOARD OBSERVATION

Players are allowed about ten seconds to observe a checkerboard on which from six to eight black checkers have been placed at random. Then the board is covered, and each player tries to duplicate the arrangement of the checkers on a checkerboard diagram (if extra checkerboards and checkers are not available). The number of checkers can be varied at will, and the difficulty will increase rapidly as the number of checkers is increased. Still greater difficulty will result if both black and white checkers are used.

3. PICTURE OBSERVATION

This game is the same as Observation, except that pictures are used instead of actual objects. Pictures cut from magazines or newspapers are pasted to a large sheet of cardboard, so that all players can see them at the same time. It is a mistake to use one large picture that includes many different objects, because there can be no agreement as to the number of objects to be named—for example, a picture of a man could be interpreted as representing a hat, coat, shoe, and so on. The proper method is to use a number of distinctly separate pictures all on one board, with the understanding that only one name is to be applied to each picture.

4. HOW WAS SHE DRESSED?

A girl with a rather unusual attire enters the room, and the players are told to observe her carefully. (She should wear or carry as many distinct articles as possible—shoes, overshoes, stockings, skirt, blouse, coat, hat, handbag, raincoat, umbrella, and so forth.) She walks around for a minute or two, chats with a few players, and then walks out. Each player must then write down as many of the articles as possible. Score one point for each article correctly listed, and subtract two for each one listed but not worn.

5. MURDER WITNESS

A small group of the players puts on for the others a short dramatic skit involving a murder. This skit does not need much polish, but it cannot be extemporaneous; it must be prepared in advance and rehearsed. At the end of the skit, each player must try to answer a number of questions about the action: What weapon was used? Who committed the murder? What did the murderer do next? Did the victim struggle?, and so on. It will be surprising to most people to see how little the players remember.

This game can be varied in a number of ways, and really requires some ingenuity for its success. In one common variation, the action takes place right in the midst of the other players. Other activities are suddenly interrupted by the entrance of two or three tough characters, who attack one of the players, kill him right in the room, and then leave.

6. WHAT CHANGE?

A number of different articles, not more than ten, are placed on a table in some simple and definite formation. Players are given about fifteen seconds to study the articles, and then must look away or leave the room. When they are again allowed to look, some of the articles have been shifted. Each player must name the articles that have been moved.

7. THE LOST CHILD

One player leaves the room, and while he is gone a second player leaves. The first player is recalled and is given ten seconds to name the missing one.

8. KALEIDOSCOPE

This game may seem easy, but it is really quite difficult. Six players, more or less, stand in a row in front of the others. The leader gives the name of a color to each of the six players. He might say "From left to right, the colors are brown, green, red, blue, yellow, and white." While the others look away, those standing in the row are completely rearranged. The others look at them again and try to name them by color.

Section II: Rigmarole games

In these games, players sit in a circle and take turns in repeating a lot of nonsense, over and over again. In nearly all cases, the nonsense is cumulative; that is, each player repeats what the last player says or does, and passes it on to the next, after adding an item of his own. The nonsense referred to may consist of words only, or it may consist of both words and motions.

9. I WENT ON A TRIP

All players are seated in a circle. One of them starts the game by saying, "I went on a trip and took my . ," naming anything at all. He might for instance say, "I went on a trip and took my raincoat." The player at his left then repeats this statement, adding a second article, as "I went on a trip and took my raincoat and my bicycle." The third player now might say, "I went on a trip and took my raincoat, my bicycle, and a waste basket." This continues, each player repeating and adding, until one fails. He has a point scored against him and begins the next inning. Naturally, the more incongruous the articles are, the better the game. The game is made more interesting by a moderate use of relatively complicated items, such as "a pair of shoestrings for my new black shoes," or "a small black book in which to record my most interesting experiences."

10. CITY OF BOSTON

Players sit in a circle, and one of them begins, "I will sell you wool when you come to the city of Boston." The next player continues, "I will sell you wool and beans when you come to the city of Boston." Each player repeats what he has heard and adds an item of his own until a player misses. He has a point scored against him and begins the next inning.

11. ONE FAT HEN

Players are seated in a circle, and the leader says, "One fat hen." This same phrase is repeated, without change or addition, by each player in turn until it comes back to the leader. The leader then prefixes a phrase that begins with the word *two* and repeats the first phrase, thus making a statement such as "Two tame turkeys and one fat hen." This entire statement is repeated by each player in turn until it has completed the circuit; then the leader starts a third statement that adds to the others a phrase beginning with three. This process is repeated until ten rounds have been made, a phrase starting with the next number being added at the beginning of each round. If a player fails to repeat the whole statement correctly, he has a point scored against him or must pay a penalty.

In principle, any phrase can be used as long as it begins with the proper number, but the phrases traditionally used are alliterative ones of three or more words each. These can hardly be invented extemporaneously, so that the game requires a leader who has the phrases ready. The following may be suggestive:

One fat hen	Six sick sisters
Two tittering titmice	Seven sallow sailors
Three thousand thrushes	Eight angelic apes
Four feeble flamingoes	Nine nice nymphs
Five furious fowls	Ten tall tree-toads

12. I WENT TO THE STORE

This game is essentially the same as I Went on a Trip, except that each added article must begin with the next letter of the alphabet. The first player says, "I went to the store and bought some artichokes" (or any other article that begins with *a*). The second player buys artichokes and also something that begins with *b*; the third player buys three articles, beginning with *a*, *b*, and *c*. Thus the fifth player might say, "I went to the store and bought some artichokes, beef, celery, dates, and endive." The game continues until a player makes a mistake in repeating what he has heard, or is unable to add an article that begins with the next letter. The latter is not very likely, since there is no restriction at all on the kind of article that can be bought.

13. MY NAME IS MARY

In this game, the rigmarole is made up of the names of the players. An object, such as a stuffed animal or rag doll, is given some fanciful or comical name and passed around the circle. If for example, the object passed is a stuffed elephant named Jumbo and it is originally held by a player named George, the game would proceed in this way: George hands the elephant to the next player, saying as he does so, "My name is George and this is Jumbo." Alice receives the elephant from George and hands it to Andy, saying, "My name is Alice and George says this is Jumbo." Andy passes it on with these words, "My name is Andy and Alice says that George says this is Jumbo." The game continues thus, each player mentioning his own name and repeating all the previous ones, until somebody makes a mistake.

14. THE CAT AND THE DOG

The players sit in a circle, and the leader holds two small objects. Any objects at all will do, such as a book and a pencil, or a small cushion and a small box. The leader turns to the player at his left, hands him one of the objects, and says as he does so, "Here is the dog." The one receiving the object says "The what?" and the leader replies, "The dog." Then the second player (the one with "the dog") hands the object to the third, saying, "Here is the dog." Number three, of course, says "The what?" Number two does not reply immediately but instead passes the question back to the leader, saying to him "The what?" "The dog" says the leader to number two; "The dog" says number two to number three. Number three now hands the dog to number four, saying "Here is the dog." "The what?" says number four to three, and the question is repeated by three to two and by two to the leader. The leader's reply, "The dog" is likewise passed from two to three and from three to four. This process continues until the dog has gone clear around the circle and back to the leader.

As soon as the leader has started the first object on its way, he starts the second one, but this time he passes it to the player at his right and says, "Here is the cat." Exactly the same rigmarole is used, except that *cat* is substituted for *dog*, so that the dog travels clockwise and the cat counterclockwise, simultaneously. Everything will probably run smoothly until the objects have traveled halfway around the circle; then they cross each other's paths, and the real fun begins.

15. WANT TO BUY A DUCK?

Players sit in a circle, and A says to B (the player on his left), "Want to buy a duck?" B asks, "Does she quack?" and A replies, "Yes, she quacks." Now B turns to the next player, C, and asks, "Want to buy a duck?" and C asks B, "Does she quack?" B passes the question on to A and when A replies to B, "Yes, she quacks," the answer is likewise repeated by B to C. The process continues in this cumulative fashion, each question about the duck's quacking being relayed back to the first player, and each reply that she does in fact quack being relayed back to the one who started the question.

There is, of course, no reason why this game should be restricted to ducks and their quacking. It works equally well with a hen that cackles, a whistle that whistles, and so on.

16. DOES SHE QUACK?

This variation of Want to Buy a Duck? incorporates the repetition of players' names as in My Name is Mary. It differs from Want to Buy a Duck? only in the way in which the answer to the question is relayed. In this case, each player must repeat all the names of players preceding him in the relay, saying for example, "Yes, Joe says that Alice says that Bill says she quacks."

17. HOW DOES SHE QUACK?

This game is identical with Want to Buy a Duck? to the point at which the player who asks the question receives his reply, but it has an additional element that involves a second trip of question and answer. When a player has been asked "Want to buy a duck?" his reply, "Does she quack?" is relayed back to the first player, and the latter's answer "Yes, she quacks" is relayed to the one who started the question, precisely as in the basic game. But the player is not satisfied, and he asks a second question, "How does she quack?" This second question is relayed back to the first player, and he replies, "Quack-quack," giving the best possible imitation of a duck. This reply is relayed to the player who started the question, who then continues the game by asking his neighbor, "Want to buy a duck?"

For simplicity, this game has been described as a variation of Want to Buy a Duck? but it can, of course, be played with the name of any animal or object that makes a sound the players can imitate. It is very successful with a flute that toots, a dog that barks, a whistle that whistles, or a cow that moos.

GROUP B: REPEAT WORDS AND ACTIONS

18. UNCLE JOSHUA DIED LAST NIGHT

"My Uncle Joshua died last night."
"That's too bad; how did he die?"
"With one eye shut, and his mouth awry,
    One foot held high, and waving goodbye."

The players sit in a circle, and the leader says to the one at his left, "My Uncle Joshua died last night." "That's too bad; how did he die?" asks the second player. The leader replies, "With one eye shut." As he says this, he closes one eye, and he must keep it closed until the end of the game. The same dialog now takes place between number two and number three, and number two must close his eye as he replies, "With one eye shut." The dialog is repeated until everyone in the circle has one eye shut. Then the leader starts the second round, saying to number two, "My Uncle Joshua died last night," and receiving the same response as before, "That's too bad; how did he die?" But this time the leader's reply to the question is different; he says, "With one eye shut and his face awry," and he suits the action to the word by screwing his mouth to one side. This process is relayed around the circle until every player has one eye shut and mouth twisted. On the third round, the leader, and every other player in turn, answers the next player's question thus, "With one eye shut, his mouth awry, and one foot held high." Of course, he now must pose with one foot held high as well as with his eye closed and his mouth twisted. During the last round, the phrase "and waving goodbye" is added, so that when the game ends every player has an eye shut, his mouth twisted, a foot held high, and his hand waving vigorously.

19. I WENT SHOPPING

One of the players in the circle, A, says to the next one, B, "I went to town." B asks, "What did you buy?" A then names any object and as he does so makes a motion suggestive of the object; for example, he may say "shoes" and shuffle his feet, or a "fountain pen" and make writing motions, or "candy" and make chewing motions. After A has replied to B and started the appropriate motion, B turns to C and remarks, "I went to town," and when C asks what he bought, he makes the same reply as A did. This goes on until all players are busily making the first motion. Then A starts the second round, names a second article, and adds a second motion to the first. One motion is added to another until some player is unable to do them all at once.

20. TOM THUMB GOT SICK

The formula for this game is precisely the same as for Uncle Joshua Died Last Night, but the words and the motions are different.

The dialog is: "Tom Thumb got sick." "How did he get sick?" "Doing this." On the first round, the reply "Doing this" is accompanied by the first motion, patting the left knee continuously with the right hand. On the second round, each player continues the first motion and adds the second, patting the right knee continuously with the left hand. There are five motions altogether, each to be done continuously, and eventually all to be done at the same time. The third motion is that of tapping the right heel on the floor; the fourth is tapping the left heel; the fifth motion is nodding the head vigorously back and forth.

21. ADD A MOTION

This game is considerably different from the preceding three. A cumulative series of actions is involved, but the actions need not be continuous; furthermore, each player adds a new action whenever his turn comes. One of the players in the circle makes any motion at all—he pats the floor with his foot, waves his arms, sticks out his tongue, or anything else that he cares to do. The second player must repeat the action of the first and simultaneously do something else. The third player must make the first two motions plus a third. Thus, the game continues, each player repeating all previous motions and adding one of his own, until someone fails. This one must pay a forfeit or have a point scored against him.

22. COLONEL BLIMP

This rigmarole is done with a tall glass containing some sort of drink. One person goes through the entire series of motions and words, and others try to duplicate them exactly. The series seems rather complicated, and few people can duplicate it correctly the first time; but the words and motions form a definite pattern, and one who analyzes the pattern should not find them too difficult. The whole series includes three rounds. The second and third rounds are the same as the first, except that everything is done twice in the second round and three times in the third. Here is how it goes:

> Pick up the glass between the thumb and one finger of the right hand, saying, "Here's to the health of Colonel Blimp."
> Take one drink from the glass and set it down on the table with one distinct tap.

Wipe the right side of an imaginary or real moustache with the right forefinger, then the left side with the left forefinger.

Tap the table at the right of the glass with the right forefinger, then at the left with the left forefinger.

Tap the under side of the table with the right forefinger and then with the left.

Stamp on the floor with the right foot and then with the left.

Rise a few inches from the chair and sit down again.

In the second round, everything is by two's, like this:

Pick up the glass between the thumb and two fingers, saying, "Here's to the health of Colonel Blimp, Colonel Blimp."

Take two drinks from the glass and set it down with two distinct taps.

Wipe the right side of the moustache twice, and then the left side twice.

Tap the table twice with the right forefinger and then twice with the left.

Tap the under side of the table twice with the right forefinger, and then twice with the left.

Stamp twice with the right foot and then twice with the left.

Rise from the chair and sit down again, twice.

On the third round, take the glass with thumb and three fingers, take three drinks, repeat "Colonel Blimp" three times, wipe the mouth three times with each forefinger, tap the top of the table and then the under side, three times with each hand, stamp three times with each foot, and rise from and sit down in the chair three times.

Section III: Finding-and-detecting games

GROUP A: FIND CONCEALED OBJECTS

23. HIDE IN SIGHT

The leader takes any small object, such as a thimble, a short pencil, or a nail, and shows it to the others. Then the others leave the room, and while they are gone the leader places the object somewhere in the room where it can be seen without anything being moved. The players come back to the room, and each tries to find the object. When one does find it, he quietly takes his seat in such a way as not to reveal the hiding place. The game continues until all are seated.

Sometimes a player is required, as he takes his seat, to call out some designated phrase, such as "Huckle Buckle Beanstalk." Another variation requires all the seated players to join in a song, each new arrival taking up the song as he takes his seat.

24. HIDE THE THIMBLE

One player tries to find a small object that has been hidden somewhere in the room by the others. As the seeker looks for the article, music is played. The loudness of the music is increased to indicate closeness to, and decreased to indicate distance from, the hidden object.

25. HIDDEN TREASURE

This game is a sort of multiple Hide in Sight. Each player is given a list of numerous small objects that have been hidden about the room. He finds the articles and indicates the location of each on a sheet of paper. The list need not be confined to concrete objects, but might include such things as a word on the cover of a book or something to be found in a picture that hangs on the wall. The winner is the one who accumulates the longest correct list within a given time.

GROUP B: DETECT A PERSON

26. WHO'S THE LEADER?

All players but one sit in a circle. While the odd man is out of the room, one of the circle players is designated leader. He starts any kind of motion that can be kept up for some time, such as slapping his knee, waving his hand, or winking one eye. All others make the same motion. When the odd man returns, the circle players are busily engaged in motioning as the leader did. Suddenly the leader changes to a different motion, and all follow him. He change. motions at frequent intervals, and all the other circle players immediately follow his lead. The odd player must find out who the leader is, that is, who is the one to start all the new motions. This can be quite difficult, and the game develops a surprising interest. When the leader is detected, he becomes the next odd man.

27. BUTTON, BUTTON

All players but one stand in a circle, each with both hands held forward, palms together. The odd man holds his hands in the same position, with a button between them. He goes to the circle players one at a time and passes his own two hands downward between those of each player in such a way that the others cannot tell whether he has left the button there or not. He moves rapidly until he has passed his hands between those of each of the others and has left the button in one of them. Then he says to all: "Button, button, who has the button?" Each player makes a guess until the one with the button is discovered. The one who makes the correct guess is next to pass the button.

28. FIND THE RING

One player stands in the center of a circle formed by the other players. The circle players hold in their hands a long string tied in a loop. A ring, through which the string passes, is shifted along the string from one player to the next, at will. The center player tries to follow the progress of the ring, and if he can call out the name of the player whose hand covers the ring, he takes his place.

29. WHERE IS THE SQUEEZE?

This game is much like Find the Ring, except that no actual object is passed. One player stands in the center of a circle formed by the others, the circle players holding hands. One player squeezes the hand of one of his neighbors, and the latter passes the squeeze to the next. The players continue to pass the squeeze along, reversing its direction as desired. The odd man tries to locate the squeeze. When he detects a player squeezing his neighbor's hand, the two trade places.

30. UP JENKINS

This game is played by two teams sitting on opposite sides of a table. The players on one side pass a silver quarter from one to another under the table. The captain of the opposing team calls, "Up, Jenkins," and all players on the team with the quarter must hold both hands up well above the table, with fists clenched. The quarter, of course, is in one of the fists. Then the captain of the opponents calls, "Down, Jenkins," and all raised hands are slapped down on the top of the table, palms flat. The opponents now try to locate the quarter. The obvious procedure would be for the captain to consult with his teammates and then to name the hand in which he thinks the coin will be found. But the method actually used is better. The empty hands are designated first, leaving the one with the coin for the last. The captain consults his men and calls out a certain hand, which is raised from the table; then a second hand, and a third, until, if the guessing team is successful, only one is left, the one that must contain the coin.

This may be thought of as a guessing game, but at its best, it is, to a great extent, a game of observation and deduction.

GROUP C: GAMES FOR AUTOMOBILE RIDERS

Of course, a great many games that are commonly played elsewhere can, with little or no adaptation, be played by those who are riding in automobiles, and it is wise for people planning trips, especially with children, to have a stock of such games ready. This section is not concerned with such games, but rather with ones that can be played *only* while riding. They are all based on the observation of things seen from the car—other cars or the roadside scene.

31. TWENTY-FIVE POINTS

Players take turns in observing the license plates of other cars; that is, the first player takes the first car, the second player the next car, and so on. Each one's score is based only on his own cars. Each player tries to find a 1 in a license number, and if there is no 1 in the number of his first car, he must wait for his next turn. After finding a 1 he looks for a 2, then a 3, and so on. For a two-digit number, the digits may be in the license number in any order; thus, the license 41659 would count for 14, 15, 16, or 19. The first player to reach 25 is the winner. Only one number can be counted for any one license plate.

32. AUTOMOBILE NINETY-NINE

Players take turns as in Twenty-five Points. Each player adds the first and last digits of the number on his first car. When his turn comes again, he adds the first and last digits and then adds this sum to the first total. He accumulates the totals until he has reached a grand total of ninety-nine. The first to do so is the winner, but all must have the same number of turns. If more than one reaches ninety-nine, the high score wins.

This game may be varied to require the winner to reach exactly the designated number of points; if he exceeds this number he begins again at zero. In this case a total of ninety-nine is too high; forty-nine is a better number.

33. TEN PAIRS

Each player selects, or is assigned, one digit. Then all players observe the license numbers of all cars, each looking for two of his own digit. The one who finds two of his digit scores a point, and the first to accumulate ten pairs is the winner. The pairs need not be together; for a player collecting sevens, 3157867 is just as good a number as 317753. There is no advantage in finding three of a digit on one plate, but four of them could count as two pairs.

34. LICENSE-PLATE POKER

Players take license plates in turn until each player has just one, and each man writes down his number. Each player makes the best poker hand possible from the digits of his number, and the best hand wins. Thus, a player with 750727 would have three sevens, whereas one with 374651 would beat him with a straight. It may be ruled that only the first five digits of each number can be considered, but it is probably better to allow all to be used; certainly better hands result from this system.

35. TEN STATES

Players take the passing cars in turn, each observing only the state in which the license was issued. The first player to accumulate ten different states is the winner.

36. LICENSE-PLATE TRAVELING

This game is especially good where a sufficient variety of license plates is to be seen, but in many situations it is not practicable. Each player selects a different destination, not too close to his own. All players observe all cars, and each man tries to find license plates from a series of states that will take him to his imaginary destination.

He may get there by a very devious route, but if he gets there first he wins.

37. NAME THE CAR

When a car is seen approaching, each player calls out his guess as to its make; the one who proves to be correct scores a point. If only two are playing and both call the same make, neither scores. If more than two are playing, those calling the same winner split the points. It may be well to delay the calling until the car is near enough for the players to base their calls on more than a pure guess.

38. ROADSIDE ANIMALS

If only two persons play, each takes one side of the road; if more than two, they divide into teams, each team taking one side. Each team counts only animals on its own side of the road. Any animal counts one point except a white horse, which counts ten. Not more than one animal of each kind can be counted in a single herd. A cemetery counts as minus ten. The first side to reach a pre-determined total, say one hundred, is the winner.

The scoring system can be varied at will, and should be modified to suit the locality and the interests of the players. Some players count one for a fowl and two for a quadruped, and some give a bonus for a cat sitting in a window.

39. SIGNBOARD ALPHABET

One player or team observes one side of the road, the other player or team the other side. Each contestant must find the letter *a* on a signboard, then the letter *b* on a later board, and so on until the alphabet is completed. Only one letter can be counted from each signboard, and the letters must be taken strictly in alphabetical order. A player is likely to find a great many *x*'s before he gets to *w*, but they will do him no good, and after *w* has been counted *x*'s may become quite rare. This game makes a good noncompetitive group activity, all players working together to find the letters.

40. ROADSIDE ALPHABET

In this game, players can work in teams or individually, and their observations are not restricted to one side of the road. Each looks for any object that begins with *a,* and the first player to call out the name of such an object gets credit for it. If an apple tree is sighted, the first to call "apple tree" gets credit for *a* and then looks for an object beginning with *b*. Meanwhile, the other players are required to find other objects beginning with *a*. After *a*, each finds an object beginning with *b*, then *c*, and so on, until the entire alphabet is completed. The letters *x* and *z* should not be required.

41. HOW FAR?

All players agree on some object or point in the distance, and each makes a guess as to how far away it is. The guesses are compared with the distance shown by the speedometer, and the closest guess wins.

42. WE'RE THERE NOW

All players agree on some object or point in the distance, and then all close their eyes. Each player, when he believes that the point has been reached, says, "We're there now" and opens his eyes. The winner is the one who makes the best estimate.

Chapter 9

WRITING GAMES

ALL THE GAMES IN THIS CHAPTER ARE PLAYED WITH PENCIL AND PAPER. Most of them are word games—based on guessing, forming, or changing words—and some of them are similar to the oral games of Chapters 5 and 7.

Section I: Word-forming games

GROUP A: ANAGRAM GAMES

Properly speaking, an anagram is a legitimate word or an intelligible phrase that is formed by rearranging the letters of another word or phrase; since either word or phrase can be formed from the other, they are said to be anagrams of each other. For example, the words *loiter* and *toiler* are anagrams of each other. The word *Easter* has at least four anagrams: *eaters, teaser, seater,* and *stares.* Other multiple anagrams are *post—pots-spot-tops, mate—meat-tame-team,* and *enlist—inlets-listen-silent-tinsel.* Some anagrams express clever ideas, such as *violet—love it,* or *the eyes—they see.*

Sometimes the letters of a word or phrase are rearranged in a form that does not make a real word, but simply a jumble of letters, such as *violet—tlivoe.* This second group of letters is not strictly an anagram of the first, since it does not make a new word, but is more accurately called a *pied word, jumbled word,* or *hashed word.* In fact, most of the games included in this section are based on jumbled words rather than on true anagrams. Because the two are used in the same way and often mixed in the same game, they are treated here as if they were the same thing.

1. ANAGRAMS

Each player is given a list of words, each of which can be re-arranged into at least one other word. The players can write the words from dictation but it is better to give each player a sheet with the words typed on it. A player is given a limited time in which to write beside each word a second word that is its anagram. For some words, it may be specified that two or even three anagrams be supplied. Some anagram combinations are listed on page 112. This game, like all the others in this section, can be played by individuals working alone, but is often better when two or three players work together as a team.

2. JUMBLED WORDS

Hashed Words. Pied Words

The leader prepares a list of words in a certain category and jumbles the letters in each word. Each player is given a list of the jumbled words (or writes them from dictation) and is allowed a limited time to write down the original words. The player with the most correct answers in the allotted time wins. Any category that is of interest to the group can be used, and there is no problem in jumbling the letters. Examples are given in the two games that follow.

3. JUMBLED CITIES

Each player is given the following list of jumbled words (or writes them from dictation) and is told to unscramble each one to form the name of an American city. After a reasonable time, the papers are collected and scored or, perhaps better, the papers are passed to other players for scoring. The person with most correct answers wins.

1. UOSHNOT
2. TROSHNALCE
3. GICHOCA
4. HARBGIMMIN
5. SNIKATYSAC
6. STRUTPHIBG
7. BLYANA
8. RIBOLATEM
9. DOVEPRINCE
10. SCHORTREE
11. SALADL
12. SIVULOLILE
13. ITHANGSNOW
14. SNOBTO
15. STREWCORE
16. DANCEVELL
17. YESRAUCS
18. TRAPNOLD
19. ROYWENK
20. MASTONACRE
21. NAPOLINESIM
22. TOREDIT
23. NAPSEKO
24. SHAVLINEL
25. NUSCOT

4. JUMBLED FRUITS AND VEGETABLES

This game is the same as Jumbled Cities, except that the words to be formed from the jumbled letters are names of well-known fruits or vegetables.

1. BEGABAC	8. TOOTAP	15. CHEAP
2. INONO	9. TROCRA	16. SCINAPH
3. TRAIPOC	10. GERANO	17. YERELC
4. TEECULT	11. CREMBUCU	18. ARDHIS
5. WRARSYTERB	12. HRBBARU	19. PEGTURFAIR
6. PURINT	13. TOOTAM	20. PLEANPIPE
7. CROWAFULILE	14. PELPA	

SOLUTION: 1. cabbage; 2. onion; 3. apricot; 4. lettuce; 5. strawberry; 6. turnip; 7. cauliflower; 8. potato; 9. carrot; 10. orange; 11. cucumber; 12. rhubarb; 13. tomato; 14. apple; 15. peach; 16. spinach; 17. celery; 18. radish; 19. grapefruit; 20. pineapple.

5. ADD-A-LETTER ANAGRAMS

The player is given a list of words, and for each word the definition of a second word. The second word in each case is to be formed from the first by adding any letter and then rearranging all the letters as desired.

1. Add a letter to *ends* and get tears asunder.
2. Add a letter to *anthem* and get a kind of gas.
3. Add a letter to *stein* and get quiet.
4. Add a letter to *ache* and get a waterfront.
5. Add a letter to *panel* and get a heavenly body.
6. Add a letter to *brute* and get a servant.
7. Add a letter to *reeling* and get undergarments.
8. Add a letter to *tone* and get a kind of singer.
9. Add a letter to *ripe* and get a steeple.
10. Add a letter to *hastens* and get shacks.

11. Add a letter to *bone* and get carried.
12. Add a letter to *much* and get pals.
13. Add a letter to *this* and get a garment.
14. Add a letter to *meets* and get units of length.
15. Add a letter to *ghosts* and get ruffians.
16. Add a letter to *poet* and get a storehouse.
17. Add a letter to *credit* and get an explosive.
18. Add a letter to *bargained* and get a kind of cloth.
19. Add a letter to *starveling* and get eternal.
20. Add a letter to *retain* and get sure.
21. Add a letter to *under* and get spoiled.
22. Add a letter to *later* and get to tell.
23. Add a letter to *least* and get a pale color.
24. Add a letter to *flirt* and get something of little importance.

SOLUTION: 1. ends–rends; 2. anthem–methane; 3. stein, silent; 4. ache–beach; 5. panel–planet; 6. brute–butler; 7. reeling–lingerie; 8. tone–tenor; 9. ripe–spire; 10. hastens–shanties; 11. bone–borne; 12. much–chums; 13. this–shirt; 14. meets–meters; 15. ghost–toughs; 16. poet–depot; 17. credit–cordite; 18. bargained–gabardines; 19. starveling–everlasting; 20. retain–certain; 21. under–ruined; 22. later–relate; 23. least–pastel; 24. flirt–trifle.

6. PROGRESSIVE ANAGRAMS

In a progressive anagram, one begins with a given word, adds any letter, and rearranges the letters to form a second word, exactly as in Add-a-Letter Anagrams. He then adds a letter to the second word, rearranges all letters to form a third word, and repeats the process as many times as required or as possible. For example, by starting with *tea* and adding letters one at a time, one can form *seat, least, pastel, apostle,* and even more words.

In the game form of this puzzle, each contestant is given the same words, say four two-letter words. He forms from each of these words, by the process just described, words of three, four, five, and six letters. The first contestant to complete a correct set of words wins. The two-letter words should consist of commonly used letters, so that a great many possibilities may be developed. Some of the best are *am, an, as, at, if, in, is, it, on,* and *to.* Some samples of progressive anagrams are listed on page 113.

Of course, this game could begin with single letters, but it seems better to start with two letters, so that all players start in the same direction. Words of seven or more letters may be required, but this will slow down the game. This is an excellent game for groups of two, three, or four players, who act as teams and collaborate in selecting the words.

7. SAMPLE ANAGRAMS

The following list gives a few anagram combinations that can be used in some of the games just described.

acme—came-mace
acre—care-race
ales—leas-seal
amble—blame
amen—mane-mean
ample—maple
argue—auger
arts—rats-star-tars
asleep—elapse-please
aster—rates-stare-
    tares-tears
astute—statue
battle—tablet
bleat—table
blister—bristle
bowl—blow
bruise—buries-rubies
cared—cedar
charm—march
cheap—peach
chesty—scythe
citadel—dialect
clasp—scalp
clean—lance
crate—trace
dale—deal-lade-lead
dare—dear-read
deigns—design-signed-
    singed
diet—edit-tide
disease—seaside

earth—heart
east—eats-sate-seat-teas
emit—mite-time
enlarge—general
enlist—inlets-listen-silent-
    tinsel
evil—live-veil-vile
filter—trifle
finger—fringe
flier—rifle
flow—fowl-wolf
fluster—restful
forest—softer
groan—organ
interrogatives—tergiver-
    sation
horse—shore
lair—liar-rail
lame—male-meal
lament—mantle
lamp—palm
laves—salve-slave-vales
leap—pale-peal-plea
least—slate-stale-steal-tales
lemon—melon
lemons—melons-solemn
limes—miles-slime-smile
loiter—toiler
low—owl
lump—plum
luster—result-rustle

marble—ramble
mate—meat-tame-team
mesa—same-seam
naps—pans-snap-span
neither—therein
nerve—never
north—thorn
panel—plane
pare—reap
part—trap-rapt
pastel—staple
paws—wasp
petal—plate-pleat
post—pots-spot-stop-tops

prides—spider
priest—sprite-stripe
reins—resin-rinse
risen—siren
salve—slave
setter—street-tester
sever—verse
silent—tinsel
sinew—swine-wines
sleet—steel
state—taste
sword—words
united—untied

8. SAMPLE PROGRESSIVE ANAGRAMS

as—sap-pals-lapse-please
at—tab-bats-baste-beasts
is—sit-this-shirt-thirst
pa—map-lamp-palms-clamps
pi—rip-pier-spire-priest-sprites
or—nor-torn-north-throne
if—fir-rift-flirt-trifle
at—sat-eats-teams-master-stammer
end—rend-under-ruined-insured
it—sit-pits-spite-stripe
in—gin-ring-grind-ringed-reading
an—tan-neat-meant-anthem
an—tan-rant-train-rating-parting
it—nit-tine-niter-retain-certain-reaction
end—dens-sends-denser-fenders
an—ant-tans-rants-strain-retains-hairnets-tarnishes-trainsheds

GROUP B: BURIED-WORD GAMES

9. BURIED WORDS

Concealed Words. Hidden Words.

A proverb or other sentence is announced, and each contestant writes it on a sheet of paper. Then he writes down as many hidden words as he can form by combining successive letters. All words must use the letters in the exact order in which they appear. No one-letter words may be used, nor any word as it appears in the original. For example, the proverb "Appearances are often deceitful" provides at least the following words: *pear, ear, ran, an, ten, tend, end, deceit,* and *it.* Although it is easy for one to overlook a word, the process of finding the words is a brief one, and players should be allowed only a very short time. At the end of the prescribed time, all should stop writing at once and the numbers of acceptable words compared.

10. BURIED CATEGORIES

Each player is given a series of sentences, with instructions to look for words in a certain category, the words being buried as in the game above. Usually, the player has a series of sentences with one word of the prescribed category buried in each, but sometimes the sentences are in a continuous paragraph with the buried words scattered at random. Players are given a short time to find the words and are scored on the number of correct ones found. The four games that follow are of the same type; others can be devised easily.

11. BURIED QUADRUPEDS

Each of the ten sentences that follow has the name of a four-footed animal buried in it.

1. Take the calico with you.
2. Your new hairdo gives you a youthful look.
3. John abhors every kind of joke.
4. On the level, I only wish to help you.
5. You can't learn this game unless you go at it more vigorously.
6. I'd rather be right than president.
7. Is this all the help I get?
8. We are invited to a dinner on Friday.
9. If you wish to develop prestige, remember your manners.
10. I hope you will try to be a very good boy.

SOLUTION: 1. cow; 2. dog; 3. horse; 4. lion; 5. goat; 6. rat; 7. pig; 8. toad; 9. tiger; 10. beaver.

12. BURIED BIRDS

Each of the following sentences conceals the name of a well-known bird. The well-informed ornithologist is warned that some of the names are general, not specific.

1. This transmitter sends out microwaves.
2. Now, let me see what you can do.
3. Do you think that Fred started all this?
4. Do you recognize a gleam in her eye?
5. I feel a distinct throb in my arm.
6. Yesterday's thaw killed our chances for skating.
7. Not more than an hour ago I saw her on the street.
8. Joe, the basketball star, lingered after the game.
9. The pigs wallowed in the mud behind the barn.
10. This is not the particular kind that I had in mind.

SOLUTION: 1. crow; 2. owl; 3. redstart; 4. eagle; 5. robin; 6. hawk; 7. heron; 8. starling; 9. swallow; 10. lark.

13. BURIED FLOWERS

Each of the following sentences conceals the name of a common flower.

1. After you wash the pans, you may prepare lunch.
2. I had to pay several taxes on this car—national tax, state tax, and city tax.
3. Did Chopin know Beethoven?
4. If this car goes any faster I will fall out.
5. The plane is now dropping food to the marooned people.
6. Before we knew it, the rhinoceros entered the water.
7. I believe it is the best plane money can buy.
8. That scow slips through the water like a rowboat.
9. I understand that the panda is your favorite animal.
10. Is your porch identical with ours?

SOLUTION: 1. pansy; 2. carnation; 3. pink; 4. aster; 5. snowdrop; 6. rose; 7. anemone; 8. cowslip; 9. daisy; 10. orchid.

14. BURIED TREES

Each of the following sentences conceals the name of a tree. As in some of the other buried-word games, the names are likely to be general, not specific.

1. John is not so good a swimmer as Henry.
2. To hem the dress, you'll have to insert a pin every inch or so.
3. If I lend you the money, you will owe me ten dollars.
4. Of what material is this mantel made?
5. The tailor gave your suit a very fancy press.
6. I hear that a bumblebee chased you.
7. If I receive the invitation, I will accept it.
8. I believe that he has them locked in the vault.
9. She sent a message to a knight in a foreign land.
10. The store had muslin, calico, poplin, denim, and other kinds of cloth.

SOLUTION: 1. ash; 2. pine; 3. willow; 4. elm; 5. cypress; 6. beech; 7. fir; 8. hemlock; 9. oak; 10. linden.

GROUP C: OTHER WORD-FORMING GAMES

15. DICTIONARY

All players are given the same long word—one of at least seven, and perhaps as many as ten or eleven, letters. Each contestant then writes down as many different words as he can form from the letters of the given word. The letters may be used in any order, and any number of letters may be used, but each word must include at least a specified minimum number of letters; this minimum is commonly three, but in some situations four is better. Thus, if the given word were *combination,* one could form a great many other words, including *comb, bomb, tin, tan,* and *notion.* Any letter may be used in a single word just as many times as it appears in the given word, and no more. Capitalized words are not permitted. A dictionary should always be at hand, and no word should be accepted unless it appears in this particular dictionary. Players are given a definite time to compile their lists; then the words are counted, and the player with the longest list wins.

16. DICTIONARY RACE

In this variation of Dictionary, the leader selects a word, from the letters of which he knows a considerable number of words can be made. He then announces a number equal to about half the total possibilities. For example, if the leader finds by advance trial that the word will produce thirty-two other words, he announces sixteen. Then all players are given the original word and directed to form from it the announced number of other words. The first to produce this number is the winner.

Section II: Word-naming games

17. INVERSIONS

Reversals

Each player is given a list of statements, each of which contains definitions or synonyms of two words. Each pair of words is such that one can be formed by spelling the other backward, as with *pin* and *nip*. Players are given a restricted time for writing the words and are scored on the basis of the number correctly named. The following are suggestive only:

1. Invert wicked and get to survive.
2. Invert a brief sleep and get a cooking vessel.
3. Invert clever and get vehicles.
4. Invert a stopper and get to swallow hastily.
5. Invert an animal pest and get a black substance.
6. Invert a snare and get to separate.
7. Invert part of a ship and get a vegetable used in soup.
8. Invert jump and get a loud tone.
9. Invert eager and get a professional singer.
10. Invert boast and get clothing.
11. Invert created and get a kind of cheese.
12. Invert a part of the mouth and get self-satisfied.
13. Invert an untruthful person and get a long narrow piece of material.
14. Invert to come together and get abounds.
15. Invert a wild animal and get a tall grassy plant.

SOLUTION: 1. evil–live; 2. nap–pan; 3. smart–trams; 4. plug–gulp; 5. rat–tar; 6. trap–part; 7. keel–leek; 8. leap–peal; 9. avid–diva; 10. brag–garb; 11. made–edam; 12. gums–smug; 13. liar–rail; 14. meet–teem; 15. deer–reed.

18. BEHEADMENTS

Decapitations

In this game, as in the preceding one, each player is given a list of statements, each statement giving clues to two words that the player is to guess. In this case, the second word of each pair is formed from the first one by dropping the initial letter, as *stone-tone*. The player scores one point for each correct answer that he is able to write down in the allotted time. Some examples follow:

1. Behead a small valley and get a beverage.
2. Behead a common fruit and get a part of the body.
3. Behead a vessel and get another part of the body.
4. Behead a dress and get a stone.
5. Behead an aquatic animal and get healthy.
6. Behead a part of a wagon and get a part of a shoe.
7. Behead part of a fence and get consumed.
8. Behead a wild animal and get a larger domestic one.
9. Behead a group of animals and get something on a door.
10. Behead brave and get aged.
11. Behead an animal den and get atmosphere.
12. Behead a place for boats and get a support for vines.
13. Behead a digging tool and get a poor dwelling.
14. Behead to gaze intensely and get a weed.
15. Behead a place for horses and get a piece of furniture.

SOLUTION: 1. vale–ale; 2. pear–ear; 3. ship–hip; 4. frock–rock; 5. whale–hale; 6. wheel–heel; 7. gate–ate; 8. fox–ox; 9. flock–lock; 10. bold–old; 11. lair–air; 12. harbor–arbor; 13. shovel–hovel; 14. stare–tare; 15. stable–table.

19. GEOGRAPHY RELAY

Players form two or more equal teams, the teams sitting in parallel lines. The man at the right end of each team has a pencil and a piece of stiff cardboard or something else on which he can write while sitting in an ordinary chair. At a signal, each man with the cardboard writes on it the name *New York* and then hands the card to the next man on his team. The second man immediately writes, below the first name, the name of any American city that is west of New York, and then hands the card to the third man. The third man writes the name of any city west of the second one, and so on until the card reaches the last man, who writes the name *San Francisco.*

Each city must be west of the one above it. The first team to travel from New York to San Francisco with a correct list of city names wins.

20. SYNONYMS

A list of from ten to twenty words is prepared, and the same list is given to all players. Each player writes beside each of the given words another word that is its synonym. He selects the *shortest* synonym he can think of. Papers are collected or traded, and the total number of letters required for all the synonyms together is counted for each player. The low score, of course, wins. For example, if one of the given words is *stop*, the player who gives *discontinue* as a synonym does not do well compared with the player who gives the word *cease*, and one who gives *end* does best of all. A disadvantage of the game is that there is always some question as to the acceptability of some words as synonyms of others.

21. STEPWORDS

Each player or competing group is given several, say five, pairs of words, the two words of each pair having the same number of letters. All contestants are given the same words. Working on one pair at a time, a contestant takes one word of the pair and changes just one letter—any letter—without altering the order of the other letters, and forms a new word; that is, he eliminates one letter and substitutes any other letter of the alphabet for it. For example, if he starts with *man* he has a great many choices: he might change the first letter so as to form *ban, can, fan, pan, ran, tan, van,* or *wan;* or he could change the second letter and form *men;* or he could change the final letter so as to form *mat, mar, mad, map,* or *maw.* He makes the same kind of change in the newly formed second word so as to form a third; he changes the third to form a fourth, and so on, until he arrives at the second word of the prescribed pair. For example, the problem of going from *dog* to *cat* could easily be solved by *dog—dot-cot-cat,* or by *dog—cog-cot-cat.* Many pairs require considerably more steps than this one, and some are impossible. In preparing the words, the leader should prefer those of three or four letters, and is seldom justified in assigning words of more than five letters. He must satisfy himself that the change from one word to the other *can* be made, although the number of steps that he himself requires is of no importance—the players may do better than he.

The contestants are given a limited time to work, sufficient time for most players to complete all the changes. Then the papers are collected and scored on the basis of the number of steps required for all the words. Naturally, the one who makes all the changes in fewest steps is the winner. A few samples of stepwords follow.

22. SAMPLE STEPWORDS

The changes in these stepwords are not necessarily made with the minimum number of steps.

1. *Bed* to *Cot:* bed—bet-let-lot—cot
2. *Black* to *White:* black—slack-slick-slice-spice-space-spade-shade-shale-whale-while—white
3. *Page* to *Book:* page—rage-race-rack-rock-rook—book
4. *Boy* to *Man:* boy—bay-may—man
5. *Call* to *Help:* call—hall-hell—help
6. *Heat* to *Cold:* heat—beat-boat-coat-colt—cold
7. *Dry* to *Wet:* dry—wry-way-wad-wed—wet
8. *Eye* to *Ear:* eye—ere-err—ear
9. *East* to *West:* east—past-pest—west
10. *Hard* to *Easy:* hard—card-cart-cast-east—easy
11. *Slow* to *Fast:* slow—blow-blot-boot-boat-coat-cost-cast—fast
12. *Fat* to *Pig:* fat—fag-fig—pig
13. *Wind* to *Gale:* wind—wine-wile-pile-pale—gale
14. *Lead* to *Gold:* lead—load-goad—gold
15. *Moon* to *Star:* moon—boon-boor-boar-soar—star
16. *Soup* to *Nuts:* soup—sous-sots-cots-cuts—nuts
17. *Sick* to *Well:* sick—silk-sill-will—well
18. *Rich* to *Poor:* rich—rice-ride-rode-role-pole-poll-pool—poor

GROUP B: INITIAL LETTER IS GIVEN

23. CATEGORIES

Guggenheim

Each player is given, or prepares for himself, a chart of horizontal and vertical lines forming rectangles or "boxes." Any number of boxes can be used, but the most common number, and probably the best, is twenty-five; that is, the chart has five horizontal rows and five vertical columns. The leader announces five categories for words, and each player writes the names of these categories at the left of the rows, one for each row. Then the leader announces five letters; these are usually, but not necessarily, letters that spell some common word. The player writes the five letters at the tops of the columns. For example, the designated categories might be flowers, cities, famous people, animals, and foods; and the letters might be *P-A-T-C-H*. Each player would then have a chart consisting of five columns with five boxes in each column, with the letter *P* at the head of the first, *A* at the second, *T* at the third, *C* at the fourth, and *H* at the fifth. The word *Flowers* would be at the left of the top row, *Cities* at the left of the second row, and so on. The player then writes down twenty-five words, one in each box; each word must belong to the category at the left of its row and must begin with the letter at the top of its column. A liberal amount of time should be allotted, so that most of the boxes will be filled. After the allotted time, the papers are traded and scored in this way:

For each acceptable word, a player scores one point for each other player who *does not have* this word. For example, if ten are playing, one who writes *Pittsburgh* for a city beginning with *P*, will probably find that some of the others have written the same word. If he should have the good luck to be the only one who names *Pittsburgh*, then he would score nine points, since there are nine other players who do not have this word; but if one other player named the same city, there would be eight players who did not do so, and each of the two with *Pittsburgh* would score eight points. Scoring is not at all difficult and is done most conveniently by trading papers and having each player call out the words on the paper that he holds.

The following sample will illustrate the game:

	P	**A**	**T**	**C**	**H**
FLOWERS	Peony	Anemone	Tiger Lily	Columbine	Hollyhock
CITIES	Pittsburgh	Ann Arbor	Tacoma	Canton	Houston
PEOPLE	Pope	Archimedes	Tennyson	Caesar	Holmes
ANIMALS	Polar bear	Anteater	Tiger	Cow	Horse
FOODS	Peaches	Artichokes	Tomatoes	Catsup	Hash

24. ONE-LETTER CATEGORIES

The players write down a relatively long list of categories—at least ten and possibly as many as twenty. A good method for selecting the categories is to allow each player in turn to name one and let all write them down as they are called. Then the leader announces a single letter, and every player tries to write one word for each of the categories, all beginning with the announced letter. The score is determined as in Categories: For each acceptable word a player scores one point for each other player who does not have it.

25. TAIL-AND-HEAD CATEGORIES

Each player prepares a chart like the one used for Categories but without letters at the tops of the columns; that is, he has five rows of five spaces each, with a different category name at the left of each row. He must write a word in each of the twenty-five spaces, five words in each category. Of the five words in each category, the first, that is, the one at the left, may begin with any letter, but the second must begin with the final letter of the first word, the third with the final letter of the second, and so on. A player's chart might look like this:

ANIMALS	Horse	Elephant	Tiger	Rabbit	Toad
STATES	Idaho	Oregon	Nevada	Arkansas	South Dakota
FLOWERS	Sweet Wm	Marigold	Dahlia	Aster	Ragged Robin
CITIES	Kalamazoo	Oshkosh	Houston	New York	Kansas City
FRUITS OR VEGETABLES	Apricot	Tangerine	Eggplant	Tomato	Orange

The game can be made more difficult by requiring that the first word in each category begin with the final letter of the last word in the preceding one. If this rule were in effect in the example above, then the first state would have to begin with *D*, since this is the last letter of the last-named animal. With this rule, it is probably better to require only four words in each category, instead of five.

In another variation, the tail-and-head idea is applied to the columns instead of the rows; that is, each word must begin with the final letter of the word just above it. Thus the words of the first (or any other) column might be: *pig—Georgia-aster-Rochester-radish.*

26. INITIAL BIOGRAPHY

For this game, each player must have a middle name; if anybody claims not to have one he is assigned one by the leader. Each player writes his three names at the top of a sheet of paper, and then the papers are passed around so that each person has a paper with another's name on it. A series of questions is to be answered; these questions can be on the paper originally, or they can be written from dictation. Each player writes for each question an answer that applies to the person whose name is at the top of the sheet. In every case, the answer must be in exactly three words, and the words must begin with the initials of the person to whom they apply. The papers are collected, shuffled, and read, each writer scoring one point for each acceptable answer. The following example will show how the game works:

1. To whom does this paper apply?	David Louis Brownell
2. What is his occupation?	Dragging large barrels
3. What is his suppressed desire?	Dating Lauren Bacall
4. What is his nature?	Darned lively bozo
5. What is his favorite pastime?	Denouncing loquacious bores
6. What does he think of the other sex?	Darling luscious bundles
7. What of his future?	Doesn't look bright
8. What is his idea of the world in general?	Danger, let's beware

27. PROGRESSIVE WORD-BOXES

Each player has a chart of five columns and seven rows, making thirty-five boxes. At the top of each column is a letter, the same for all players, and at the left of each row is a number; the numbers, from top to bottom, are 4, 5, 6, 7, 8, 9, and 10. The player is required to write a word in each of the thirty-five boxes, each word beginning with the letter at the top of the column and containing as many letters as designated by the number at the left of the row. There are no categories, and any words at all may be used as long as they meet the requirements of initials and length. Players are given a prescribed time to fill in the boxes; then the papers are scored, one point for each acceptable word. If the prescribed letters were T-A-B-L-E, a player's chart might look like this:

	T	A	B	L	E
4	take	able	bent	lost	ends
5	table	after	broke	leans	earth
6	tanned	autumn	breeze	larger	ending
7	tarnish	against	bending	likened	exactly

T	A	B	L	E
8 tomatoes	autumnal	bundling	loosened	enervate
9 tabulated	aggressor	bombastic	lessening	ectoplasm
10 thereafter	aggregates	bedraggled	luminosity	encyclical

Of course, other word lengths may be prescribed; sometimes another row is added for words with any number of letters greater than ten.

GROUP C: OTHER LETTERS ARE PRESCRIBED

28. WORD ENDINGS

Each player is given, or writes from dictation, a list of word endings, about twenty of them. These word endings are not necessarily syllables, but each is any combination of letters, usually three, that form the endings of common words, such as *und, mes, tch, nty, noe, uit, ket, wly, ter, ner, her, ain, ose, ene, nse, ken, ady, ely, ity,* and *don*. The player is given a limited time to complete words, one for each given ending, and is scored on the basis of the number he has correct. Any recognized uncapitalized word is acceptable, regardless of length. For example, the first three of the endings above might be used in the words *sound, dames, itch,* and *twenty*.

29. FILL-INS

Each player is given the first and last letters of a series of four-letter words, as *l——p, b——k*. Within a limited time, he is required to supply the missing letters so as to complete the list of words, and scores one point for each acceptable word. The list should be fairly long, consisting of thirty or forty words. This game, like similar ones, is essentially a test of speed, and for this reason all players must be given the same amount of time. Only well-known words should be selected. Completing such words may appear easy enough, but when one is pressed for time, it is surprising how difficult it may be to complete *l——p* as *lamp* and *f——k* as *fork*.

The game can be varied, of course, by calling for words of five, or even six, letters each.

30. ACROSTIC CONTEST

A word of five, six, or seven letters is announced, and each player writes the letters of this word in a column down the left side of a sheet of paper; he then writes the same word in a parallel column to the right of the first one, but this time in reverse order; for example:

B	T
A	E
S	K
K	S
E	A
T	B

He now proceeds to write words (six of them in the example given) beginning and ending with the given letters, in each case writing the *longest* word that he can think of. He scores one point for each letter used in an acceptable word. For example, *BET* is correct for the first word in the example, but it scores only three points; *BENT* is a little better, scoring four; *BOMBAST* is still better, scoring seven.

31. LONG-WORD GAME

This game is much the same as Acrostic Contest, except for the location of the prescribed letters. Each player is given a list of about ten combinations of two or three letters each and is required to incorporate each combination in a word, the longest word possible. Any combination of letters can be used, but it is best to use those that are not commonly found at the beginnings or ends of words, for example *bn, utu, ino, gg, ndl, nc.* Each letter correctly used scores one point. Thus for *nc*, the word *inch* scores four points, but *encyclopedia* scores twelve.

32. SHORT-WORD GAME

This game is the same as Long-Word Game, except that the players write the *shortest* words possible. Each player's score is determined by counting the letters in all his words, and the low score wins. The prescribed letters must be selected so as not to suggest obvious three-letter words.

Section III: Composition and drawing games

This section includes games or stunts in which the players compose verse, write prose, or produce drawings. They are similar to some kinds of puzzles, but are not puzzles because they do not have correct and incorrect answers—only answers that are more or less clever.

33. TELEGRAMS

The leader dictates fifteen letters, and each player writes a telegram of fifteen words, using as initials the assigned letters in correct order. The dictated letters may be chosen at random, or may make up a word or group of words appropriate to the occasion.

34. CRAMBO

Crambo is a very old game. Each player is given a question and an entirely unrelated noun, either common or proper. The leader may prepare the questions and nouns in advance, then shuffle and distribute them; or, if preferred, each player may be asked to write a question on one slip of paper and a noun on another, the slips being then shuffled and drawn by the players. Any kind of questions may be used; for example, "Do you like peonies?" "Who is Liberace?" "How many sides has a tetrahedron?." Also, any nouns are acceptable: cat, George Washington, boy, telegram, or anything at all.

Having drawn, or been given, a question and a noun, each player is required to write a poem that answers the question and uses the noun in doing so. Most of the poems are likely to be far-fetched and not very good, but all will be good fun and a few of them very clever indeed. Suppose one of the less clever poets should draw the question, "When did Columbus discover America?" and the noun "telegram." He might concoct this:

> I've been informed by telegram,
> And I do believe it's true,
> That Columbus discovered America
> In fourteen ninety-two.

35. PROGRESSIVE POEMS

Each player writes the first line of a verse, either a quotation from a well-known poem, or one that he composes for the occasion. He folds the paper so that his line cannot be seen, copies the last word below the fold, and hands the paper to the next player. The latter then writes a second line that rhymes with the first, folds the paper again, and hands it to the third player. The process is repeated once more, so that the result is a four-line poem with all lines rhyming. Another method is to have the poem consist of a series of couplets, no couplet rhyming with any other. In any case, it is important that the meter of the lines of any poem be the same. The easiest and best way to make sure that they are the same is for the leader to specify the meter and line length in advance.

36. WANT ADS

Each player is given the classified advertisement section of a newspaper. Scissors, paste, and sheets of paper should also be available. The player clips words, phrases, or sentences from the advertisements and recombines them by pasting them to a sheet of paper. His object is to make a synthetic advertisement of a comical or incongruous nature. The finished products are exchanged and read.

37. BLIND DRAWING

With all lights out, or while blindfolded, each player draws a picture of any assigned simple object, such as a house or a pig. After they have finished the first assignment and have had an opportunity to relax, he calls for further drawing. For example, he might assign a house and then, apparently as an afterthought, call for a walk leading to the house, or smoke coming from the chimney.

38. SELF-PORTRAIT

A player has a large paper bag slipped over his head (no holes for eyes). Then, with a piece of charcoal or other very soft drawing material, he draws a picture of his own face on the sack. His attempts to do so are likely be to very amusing.

Section IV: Conundrum games

A conundrum is a riddle based on a pun. In most cases the pun is in the answer, as in "What author is good for breakfast?" (*Bacon*). In some cases, however, the pun is in the question, as in "What grows bigger the more you *contract* it?" (A debt). A conundrum game is simply a collection of conundrums with a pun in each answer and with all answers in a prescribed category. The category may be a class of real things, such as trees, flowers, or cities (here called a *Straight Conundrum Game*). On the other hand, the category may be an artificial one, based only on the *sound* of the word or words in the answer (here called a *Phonetic Conundrum Game*).

Every player is given a list of the questions and is required to supply the answers within a limited time. It is best to have the questions typed in advance. Each player scores one point for each correct answer. It is certain that some answers will be different from the anticipated ones and still completely correct; such answers should be given full credit.

GROUP A: STRAIGHT CONUNDRUM GAMES

39. WHAT FLOWER?

1. What flower is what a man did when he proposed?
2. What flower do unmarried men often lose?
3. What flower results from Cupid's arrows?
4. What flower is a pretty girl who has been jilted?
5. What flower is a dairy product and a dish?
6. What flower is a country with lots of automobiles?
7. What flower is an animal's mistake?
8. What flower is a dressed-up ferocious animal?
9. What flower is a sweetheart's farewell?
10. What flower is the time for tea?
11. What flower is part of an eye?
12. What flower is a preacher?
13. What flower is what Father says to John in the morning?
14. What flower is a man's name and what he writes it with?
15. What flower is footwear?
16. What flower is a bird and a riding accessory?
17. What flower is between hills?
18. What flower is a way for a man to get rich quick?
19. What flower suggests the rising sun?
20. What flower do shepherds watch?
21. What flower is neat rows?
22. What flower is a tattered bird?
23. What flower is what Johnny did when he sat on a tack?
24. What flower is fragrant letters?

25. What flower is an amiable man?
26. What flowers are the place for a kiss?

ANSWERS: 1. aster; 2. bachelor buttons; 3. bleeding heart; 4. bluebell; 5. buttercup; 6. carnation; 7. cowslip; 8. dandelion; 9. forget-me-not; 10. four o'clock; 11. iris; 12. jack-in-the-pulpit; 13. johnny-jump-up; 14. jonquil; 15. lady's slipper; 16. larkspur; 17. lily of the valley; 18. marigold; 19. morning glory; 20. phlox; 21. primrose; 22. ragged robin; 23. rose; 24. sweet peas; 25. sweet william; 26. tulips.

40. WHAT TREE?

1. What tree is found after a fire?
2. What tree tells what a boy does when he has been spanked?
3. What tree is nearest the sea?
4. What tree is a worn-out joke?
5. What tree is often found in bottles?
6. What tree keeps a lady warm?
7. What tree is an insect?
8. What tree does everyone carry in his hand?
9. What tree suggests a parent?
10. What tree is a pretty girl?
11. What tree is a couple?
12. What is the straightest tree that grows?
13. What tree is in high favor?
14. What is the neatest tree?
15. What tree grieves most?
16. What tree is older than most others?
17. What tree is a carpenter's tool?
18. What tree is a body of water?
19. What tree marks the advance of time?
20. What tree sighs and languishes?

ANSWERS: 1. ash; 2. balsam; 3. beech; 4. chestnut; 5. cork; 6. fir; 7. locust; 8. palm; 9. pawpaw; 10. peach; 11. pear; 12. plum; 13. poplar; 14. spruce; 15. weeping willow; 16. elder; 17. plane; 18. bay; 19. date; 20. pine.

41. WHAT LETTER OF THE ALPHABET?

1. What letter is an insect?
2. What letter is a body of water?
3. What letter is a river in Scotland?
4. What letter is a command to a horse?
5. What letter is in the head?

6. What letter is a bird?
7. What letter is part of a house?
8. What letter is a printer's measure?
9. What letter means to be indebted?
10. What letter is a spring vegetable?
11. What letter is an actor's signal?
12. What letter is a beverage?
13. What letter is a sheep?

ANSWERS: 1. *B*; 2. *C*; 3. *D*; 4. *G*; 5. *I*; 6. *J*; 7. *L*; 8. *M*; 9. *O*; 10. *P*; 11. *Q*; 12. *T*; 13. *U*.

42. WHAT LETTERS?

1. What two letters are a number?
2. What two letters describe a snake's eyes?
3. What two letters mean poorly dressed?
4. What two letters mean to rot?
5. What two letters mean not difficult?
6. What two letters mean results?
7. What two letters mean cold?
8. What two letters are a vine?
9. What two letters are a kind of pepper?
10. What two letters are a girl's name?
11. What two letters mean vacant?
12. What two letters mean jealousy?
13. What two letters are a kind of cloth?
14. What two letters mean an attractive girl?
15. What two letters are a written composition?
16. What two letters are a county in England?
17. What two letters are a tent used by American Indians?
18. What two letters mean to surpass others?
19. What two letters mean superfluous?
20. What double letter contains a great deal of water?
21. What double letter means comfort?
22. What double letter means what bad boys do?
23. What double letter means not ignorant?
24. What three letters mean a funeral poem?
25. What three letters mean a foe?
26. What three letters are something of which a small boy has a lot?

27. What three letters mean a place of quiet pleasure?
28. What three letters mean happiness?
29. What four letters mean a person has been found?
30. What five letters mean fitness?
31. What two letters and a number mean a drug?

ANSWERS: 1. *A-T*; 2. *B-D*; 3. *C-D*; 4. *D-K*; 5. *E-Z*; 6. *F-X*; 7. *I-C*; 8. *I-V*;
9. *K-N*; 10. *K-T* or *L-C*; 11. *M-T*; 12. *N-V*; 13. *P-K*; 14. *Q-T*; 15. *S-A*; 16. *S-X*;
17. *T-P*; 18. *X-L*; 19. *X-S*; 20. *CC* (seas); 21. *EE* (ease); 22. *TT* (tease);
23. *YY* (wise); 24. *L-E-G*; 25. *N-M-E*; 26. *N-R-G*; 27. *R-K-D*; 28. *X-T-C*;
29. *O-I-C-U*; 30. *X-P-D-N-C*; 31. *O-P-8*.

43. APPROPRIATE CAKE

1. What cake would you bake for the Devil?
2. What cake would you bake for a farmer?
3. What cake would you bake for lovers?
4. What cake would you bake for a geologist?
5. What cake would you bake for an idler?
6. What cake would you bake for a sculptor?
7. What cake would you bake for a politician?
8. What cake would you bake for a monkey?
9. What cake would you bake for a dog-catcher?
10. What cake would you bake for a gossip?
11. What cake would you bake for one who lives on his friends?
12. What cake would you bake for a convalescent?

ANSWERS: 1. angel food; 2. fruit cake; 3. kisses; 4. layer cake; 5. loaf cake;
6. marble cake; 7. plum cake; 8. coconut cake; 9. pound cake; 10. spice cake;
11. sponge cake; 12. sunshine cake.

44. APPROPRIATE FOOD

1. What food is appropriate for a teacher?
2. What food is appropriate for a baseball player?
3. What food is appropriate for a policeman?
4. What food is appropriate for a woodworker?
5. What food is appropriate for a jeweler?
6. What food is appropriate for a chiropodist?
7. What food is appropriate for an electrician?
8. What food is appropriate for an actor?
9. What food is appropriate for a traffic officer?
10. What food is appropriate for a plumber?
11. What food is appropriate for newlyweds?

12. What food is appropriate for a printer?
13. What food is appropriate for a pugilist?
14. What food is appropriate for a shoemaker?
15. What food is appropriate for a gambler?

ANSWERS: 1. alphabet noodles; 2. batter cakes; 3. beets; 4. cabinet pudding; 5. carrots; 6. corn; 7. currants; 8. ham; 9. jam; 10. leeks; 11. lettuce alone; 12. pie; 13. punch; 14. sole; 15. steaks.

45. WHICH STATE?

Each question refers to a state in the United States, but is to be answered by the *abbreviation* of the state's name.

1. Which state is Mohammedan?
2. Which state saved Noah?
3. Which state is the nickname of a former president?
4. Which state means "to study carefully"?
5. Which state is a girl's name?
6. Which state is in poor health?
7. Which state is used for preserving food?
8. Which state is a physician?
9. Which state is a church service?
10. Which state is most egotistical?
11. Which state is a character in a comic strip?
12. Which state is a young girl?
13. Which state means to cut grass?
14. Which state is a large hill?
15. Which state is an exclamation?
16. Which state is a mineral?
17. Which state is a parent?
18. Which state is a writing instrument?
19. Which state is a grain?
20. Which state is a number?
21. Which state is a boy's nickname?
22. Which state is the cleanest?

ANSWERS: 1. Ala.; 2. Ark.; 3. Cal.; 4. Conn.; 5. Ida.; 6. Ill.; 7. Kan.; 8. Md.; 9. Mass.; 10. Me.; 11. Minn.; 12. Miss.; 13. Mo.; 14. Mont.; 15. O.; 16. Ore.; 17. Pa.; 18. Penn.; 19. R.I.; 20. Tenn.; 21. Tex.; 22. Wash.

46. WHICH BOOK OF THE BIBLE?

1. Which book of the Bible means records?
2. Which book of the Bible is a boy's name and a loud cry?
3. Which book of the Bible is what you water the garden with, plus *A*?
4. Which book of the Bible is a position to earn money?
5. Which book of the Bible means rulers?
6. Which book of the Bible means to take notice?
7. Which book of the Bible is a brand of tobacco?
8. Which book of the Bible is a kind of grass?
9. Which book of the Bible is a Roman emperor?

ANSWERS: 1. Chronicles; 2. Daniel; 3. Hosea; 4. Job; 5. Kings; 6. Mark; 7. Revelation; 8. Timothy; 9. Titus.

GROUP B: PHONETIC CONUNDRUM GAMES

In the conundum games described above, each question is to be answered with the actual name of a member of the category referred to; for example, the question, "What tree is _____?" must be answered by "oak," or "hemlock," or the name of some other tree. A phonetic conundrum game is different, for here the answer is not the actual name of a member of the class referred to, but instead a word, of any kind at all, that includes the *sound* prescribed by the question. For example, the question "What tree _____?" could be answered (if appropriate) by "pan*try*," or "en*try*," or "devil*try*." Such conundrums are easily devised, and a list can readily be made on the basis of some word appropriate to a particular occasion. The following examples are only a small sample of possible ones.

47. WHAT AGE?

1. What age do travelers use?
2. What age is a drink?
3. What age is a vehicle?
4. What age is a game?
5. What age will we reach if we live long enough?
6. At what age do many people marry?
7. What age do birds have?
8. What is a canoeist's age?

9. What is a letter's age?
10. What is a butcher's age?
11. What is a football player's age?
12. What is an electrician's age?

ANSWERS: 1. baggage; 2. beverage; 3. carriage; 4. cribbage; 5. dotage; 6. parsonage; 7. plumage; 8. portage; 9. postage; 10. sausage; 11. scrimmage; 12. voltage.

48. WHAT CAT?

1. What cat is a subterranean cemetery?
2. What cat has fits?
3. What cat lists things for sale?
4. What cat is a tree?
5. What cat is used for shooting?
6. What cat is a waterfall?
7. What cat is a calamity?
8. What cat is a variety of a popular fruit?
9. What cat goes to Sunday School?
10. What cat is a class of things?
11. What cat is curved?
12. What cat is a small fuzzy animal?
13. What cat is aromatic?
14. What cat is a condiment?
15. What cat is a ranchman's cat?

ANSWERS: 1. catacomb; 2. catalepsy; 3. catalog; 4. catalpa; 5. catapult; 6. cataract; 7. catastrophe; 8. catawba; 9. catechism; 10. category; 11. catenary; 12. caterpillar; 13. catnip; 14. catsup; 15. cattle.

49. WHAT NATION?

1. What nation is most hated?
2. What nation is murderous?
3. What nation is a flower?
4. What nation worked for prohibition?
5. What nation is convicted?
6. What nation is fearful?
7. What nation is topmost?
8. What nation is condemned?
9. What nation is a religious sect?
10. What nation is a goal?

11. What nation is resolute?
12. What nation is unfair?
13. What nation is scattered?
14. What nation tells fortunes?
15. What nation is a gift?
16. What nation expels?
17. What nation is dreaded by students?
18. What nation is destructive?
19. What nation is most charming?
20. What nation sees imaginary things?
21. What nation is brightest?
22. What nation is fanciful?
23. What nation is an actor?
24. What nation is angry?
25. What nation is disobedient?
26. What nation puts everything off?
27. What nation is made young?
28. What nation is at the end?

ANSWERS: 1. abomination; 2. assassination; 3. carnation; 4. Carrie Nation; 5. condemnation; 6. consternation; 7. culmination; 8. damnation; 9. denomination; 10. destination; 11. determination; 12. discrimination; 13. dissemination; 14. divination; 15. donation; 16. elimination; 17. examination; 18. extermination; 19. fascination; 20. hallucination; 21. illumination; 22. imagination; 23. impersonation; 24. indignation; 25. insubordination; 26. procrastination; 27. rejuvenation; 28. termination.

50. WHAT T?

1. What T is capable?
2. What T is ridiculous?
3. What T is nimble?
4. What T is worried?
5. What T is attractive?
6. What T is short?
7. What T is a measure of ability to hold?
8. What T is unselfish?
9. What T has lots of people?
10. What T killed a cat?
11. What T lasts a long time?
12. What T stretches?
13. What T lights our homes?

14. What T lasts forever?
15. What T is happy?
16. What T is savage?
17. What T is brotherhood?
18. What T is cold?
19. What T is proud?
20. What T is weak?
21. What T is always brave?
22. What T cannot be seen?
23. What T is generous?
24. What T is powerful?
25. What T is aristocratic?
26. What T is new?
27. What T is devout?
28. What T comes first?
29. What T is successful?
30. What T is prompt?
31. What T has a slow wit?
32. What T is frugal?
33. What T is changeable?
34. What T is speedy?

ANSWERS: 1. ability; 2. absurdity; 3. agility; 4. anxiety; 5. beauty; 6. brevity; 7. capacity; 8. charity; 9. city; 10. curiosity; 11. durability; 12. elasticity; 13. electricity; 14. eternity; 15. felicity; 16. ferocity; 17. fraternity; 18. frigidity; 19. haughty; 20. infirmity; 21. intrepidity; 22. invisibility; 23. liberality; 24. mighty; 25. nobility; 26. novelty; 27. piety; 28. priority; 29. prosperity; 30. punctuality; 31; stupidity; 32. thrifty; 33. variety; 34. velocity.

Chapter 10

TABLE AND BOARD GAMES

ALL THE MOST HIGHLY DEVELOPED INDOOR GAMES ARE IN THE TABLE and Board Class—all standard card games of the whist, poker, rummy, and other families; checkers and chess; dominoes in its various forms; backgammon, and many others. This book does not deal with such formalized games but describes only games that are informal and that can be played successfully without preparation. These informal games will be presented in three groups: card games, move games, and dice games.

Section I: Informal card games

1. OH HELL

Although this game is similar to Contract Bridge, it does not require familiarity with that game; it can be learned in five minutes by one who has never heard of Bridge Whist of any sort. The game could be played after a fashion by from two to twenty-six players, but it is recommended for groups of from three to nine and is at its best with from four to seven players. It is played with a standard Bridge deck of fifty-two cards.

The players sit around a table, and one of them deals the cards after they have been shuffled and cut. He deals to the players in clockwise order, beginning with the one at his left and ending with himself. He deals one card at a time and continues until the number of cards remaining is insufficient for another complete round. He then stops dealing and places the remaining cards, if any, face down on the table. If nine play, each will get five cards; if eight play, each will get six; and if five play, each will get ten. The dealer now takes the top card of the few that he has just placed on the table and turns it face up for all to see. This card determines the trump suit in the hand about to be played and has no other significance; its rank is of no consequence, only its suit. If the cards come out exactly even on the deal, so that there are no cards remaining to be placed on the table, then the hand is played at No Trump. Each player knows that the number of tricks in the hand about to be played is the same as the number of cards he holds; he also knows which suit will be trump.

Beginning with the dealer and going clockwise around the table, each player in turn announces the exact number of tricks that he proposes to take in the hand, any number from zero to all. These numbers, or *bids,* must be written down by one of the players selected to act as scorekeeper. Next, the player at the left of the dealer takes a card from his hand—any card he chooses to play—and plays it face up in the middle of the table. The other players in order play one card each, all these cards together constituting the first trick. In playing his card, every player must follow these basic laws of Bridge (they are really laws of Whist, from which all forms of Bridge are derived.):

(*a*) He must follow suit if possible; that is, if he has in his hand any card of the suit led (the first card played) he must play it, and if he has more than one such card he may choose any one of them.

(*b*) If his hand includes no card of the suit led, he may play any card at all; in this case, he will often elect to play a card of the trump suit, but he need not, and often will prefer not to do so.

The object of each player is to win the exact number of tricks that he has bid—no more and no less. Obviously, then, he will sometimes try to win a trick and at other times try not to win, but he may be forced to win a trick against his will. The winner of a trick is determined by these simple rules:

(*a*) If a trick includes one or more cards of the trump suit, the highest trump card wins the trick; often, the trick contains only one trump card, and such a card wins regardless of its rank.

(*b*) If a trick does not include a trump card, then it is won by the highest card of *the suit led.* The highest card in any suit is always the ace, then in order the king, queen, jack, 10, 9, 8, 7, 6, 5, 4, 3, 2.

Whoever wins the first trick plays the first card for the second, and again he may play any card whatever, the others following in clockwise order. This process is continued until all the cards have been played. When all the tricks of the first hand have been played, the number won by each player is compared with his bid. If the numbers are not the same, the player gets no score and no penalty. If they are the same, he scores ten points plus the number of tricks bid and made; that is, one who bids four and takes exactly four scores fourteen points, while one who bids and takes two scores twelve points.

When the first hand has been played and scored, the cards are collected, shuffled, and dealt, the dealer this time being the player at the left of the first one. On the second hand, the dealer gives each player one card less than he did for the first hand; otherwise, the two hands are identical. Then a third hand is dealt, each player getting one card less than for the second, a fourth hand with still one card less, and so on until the last hand is played with each player getting just one card.

Sometimes the scoring system is varied to provide that a player who bids and takes all the tricks (a grand slam) gets a bonus of fifty points, and one who bids and takes all but one (small slam) gets a bonus of twenty-five. If this bonus system is adopted, it should be used only with hands of five or more cards.

Instead of beginning with the largest hand and working down to the smallest, it is possible to reverse the process; that is, to begin with a hand of one card and increase the number by one on each succeeding deal.

2. DONKEY

This game can be played by any number of people from three to thirteen. A standard deck of cards is used but, unless thirteen players are in the game, some of the cards are removed from the deck. For twelve players the four twos are eliminated, for eleven the twos and threes, and so on, until only enough cards remain to deal four to each player. The cards are dealt one at a time. The dealer then gives the command "Go," and each player takes any card from his own hand and passes it face down to the one at his left, at the same time, of course, receiving one from the player at his right. He adds the card just received to the three remaining in his hand and without delay passes any one of the four to the left and picks up a new one from his right. The players continue, without delay or signal, to pass and receive cards, hoping to get all four cards of the same denomination—four twos, four queens, or four sevens, for example.

As soon as any player has acquired all four cards of any denomination, he lays them down on the table and places one finger along the side of his nose, doing both these things as quietly and inconspicuously as possible. As soon as another player sees this, he also lays his cards down and places his finger along his nose. The last one to do these things is a "donkey." The game is repeated until someone has been donkey for a specified number of times. Sometimes the game is continued until one player has been donkey six times, the score being kept by writing one letter of the word *donkey* beside the name of a player each time he loses.

3. CONCENTRATION

An entire deck of cards is shuffled and dealt face down in several rows. The exact pattern of the cards is not important, but it must be reasonably regular so that each card has a definite place. The first player picks up any two cards and lets all the players see them. If, by chance, he picks up two cards of the same rank, such as two queens or two sevens, he keeps the cards and plays again, continuing until he fails to pick up a pair. When he picks up two cards that are not a pair, either on his first play or later, he simply replaces them face down and waits for his next turn. The other players in turn do the same thing, but each player after the first has the advantage of perhaps remembering the location of cards that have been replaced. The game continues until all cards have been removed. The player with the most cards wins.

4. MENAGERIE

This hilarious game can be played by three or more people. It is better with two decks of cards, and with large groups even three or four decks; all the cards are shuffled together and treated as a single deck. The cards are dealt one at a time until they are all given out; it does not matter if some players have one card more than others. Each player must have the name of some animal, either domestic or wild. There are various ways of selecting the animals, but probably the best method is for the leader to select animal names in advance and let the players draw them by lot. Each player, without looking at his cards, places them face down in a pile in front of him.

The player at the dealer's left begins the game by turning over the top card on his pile so as to start a new pile, face up. Then the second player turns a card, next the third player, and so on. After the first round, the turning of cards continues without interruption for as many rounds as necessary. When all the cards that a player has are in his face-up pile, he simply turns the pile over and continues.

When a card just turned over is of the same rank as any one of the other cards already showing, each of the two players with the matching cards must immediately call out the name of the animal represented by *the other*. The one who makes a correct call first takes his whole pile of face-up cards and adds them to the face-up pile of the other, placing them on the bottom. This continues until some player wins the game by getting rid of all his cards.

5. AUTHORS

In its original form, Authors was played with special cards, each card having on it the picture of an author and either a quotation from, or the name of, one of his works. As described here, the game is to be played with a standard deck. It is best with from four to eight players. The entire deck is dealt out even though some players get one card more than others.

Each player must acquire as many "books" as possible, a book consisting of the four cards of any rank, such as four eights or four kings. To start the game, the player at the left of the dealer turns to any other player and asks him for a card of any particular denomination, saying, for example, "Please give me a seven." If the one addressed has a card of the rank mentioned, he must give it up; furthermore, if he has more than one he must give them all, even though only one is requested. A player is not permitted to ask for a card unless he already holds at least one of the same denomination. If he is successful the first time, that is, if he gets the card asked for, then he tries again and continues until he fails. Then the next player tries, and the others in turn.

Obviously, the players soon acquire valuable information about the location of cards and are very likely to take from one man the cards that he has just received from another. As soon as a player has all four cards of any denomination, he must show them and lay them down. Play continues until all the cards have been formed into books and have been laid down, and each player scores one point for each of his books. The game may be varied to require that a man asking for a card name both its rank and its suit.

6. GO FISH

This game is sometimes considered a variation of Authors and is often preferred to the basic form. It uses a full standard deck and will accommodate from three to six players. On the deal each player is given five cards, and the remaining cards are stacked on the table, face down, as the "fish pond." The object of the game is the same as that of Authors, that is, to form books, each book consisting of the four cards of any one rank.

The first player names any specific card, by suit and rank, and asks any other player for it. If he gets the card, he calls for another, not necessarily from the same player, and continues until he fails. When he fails he must draw the top card from the fish pond and add it to his hand. Players take turns around the table, each trying to form books and placing them on the table when completed. Play continues until one man gets rid of all his cards.

7. OLD MAID

This game is played with a standard deck of cards, except that one of the queens is discarded, leaving fifty-one cards. Also, for a small group of players the size of the deck may be reduced, if desired, by removing some of the lowest ranking cards, always in groups of four; for example, all the twos and threes might be eliminated. All the cards are dealt, one at a time, even though they do not come out even. Each player removes from his hand any pairs that may be there, and places them face down before him; these cards must be in twos, not threes, although four of a kind are, of course, discarded as two pairs.

Now the dealer fans out the cards in his hand and holds it up to the player at his left, who takes one of the cards, of course without knowing what it is. Then the third player draws a card from the hand of the second, the fourth from the third, and so on around the circle as many times as necessary. Whenever a player draws a card that matches one already in his hand—that is, one of the same rank

—he discards the pair, and play continues until all the cards in the game have been discarded except one. This one card must be, of course, the odd queen or "Old Maid." The player who holds the Old Maid at the end of the hand is the loser. Other hands are played until one player has lost ten times; at this point the one who has lost the fewest times is the winner.

8. WILD EIGHTS

Crazy Eights. Dirty Eights.

This is a good game for two or more players. A standard deck is used, and if more than four play it is better to use two decks. Cards are dealt one at a time until each player has seven, and the remaining cards are stacked face up on the table as the "stock." The player at the dealer's left begins the game by taking any card at all from his hand and placing it face up on the table. The next man may then play from his hand any card that matches the first one either in rank or in suit; for example, if the first man plays the six of clubs, then the second may play any other six or any other club. If this player has an eight-spot in his hand, he may play it no matter what its suit. Furthermore, he has the right to call it the eight of any suit at all, regardless of its actual suit. For example, if the first man has played the jack of spades, the second man might lay down the eight of diamonds, saying as he does so, "Eight of clubs." This card must then be played to as if it actually were the eight of clubs. Of course, the eight of the suit first played is no exception to this rule, so that in the example given the second player could play the eight of spades but call it the eight of clubs, or diamonds.

If the player is unable to match the suit or rank of the first card, or to play an eight, he must draw a card from the stock and continue to draw until he is able to play. A very important rule is that a player is permitted to draw cards from the stock even though he is able to play a card from his hand. Of course, he runs a risk of being caught with cards that count against him, but he may draw whenever it is his turn to play and may draw as many cards as he cares to. Thus, the second man must eventually play a card, either one that matches the first card or an eight; he always plays just one card at each turn. When the second man has played, the third one plays to the second card in exactly the same way: he may play a matching card from his hand, he may play an eight, or he may draw and then play.

The hand is completed when any player gets rid of all his cards. Then each player scores negative points for the cards remaining in his hand, and the winner scores positive points equal to the sum of the negative ones. For this purpose, an eight counts fifty points; an ace, king, queen, jack, or ten counts ten points; all other cards count their face values. The first player to reach a designated total, say five hundred, is winner of the match.

9. NEWMARKET

Michigan Boodle. Stops.

This game can be played by from three to eight people. It requires a standard deck and in addition four cards from another deck—an ace, a king, a queen, and a jack, all in different suits. Each player has a supply of chips or counters. The four extra cards, called "Boodle Cards," are placed face up on the table, and before the cards are dealt each player places four of his chips on these cards; he may place all four chips on any one card or he may divide them among the four cards in any way that he chooses. The cards are dealt one at a time, with an extra hand as if there were one more player in the game. All cards are dealt even though the hands do not contain the same number of cards.

Before play begins, the dealer examines his hand, and if he cares to do so he discards it and takes the extra hand instead. If he decides to keep his original hand, he auctions off the extra one, giving it to the player who offers the largest number of chips. This player then takes the extra hand to play with and discards his original one.

The player at the dealer's left begins the hand by playing a card; this card may be of any suit, but it must be the lowest of his cards in the selected suit. Then the next higher card in the same suit is played by whichever player happens to have it, then the next, and so on, if possible until the highest card of the suit—the ace—is played. It may be that at some point the next higher card cannot be played because it is in the extra hand; in this case a "stop" is reached. Then the player who has played the last card plays again, this time his lowest card in any suit other than that of the last card played, and play goes on as before; it may be that he does not have a card in any other suit and if so he cannot play. Then the right to do so passes to the next player. In this series or in any later one a stop may be reached because the next card has been played in an earlier series.

There are two objectives to the game. The first is to play a card that matches one of the boodle cards, and one who does so collects immediately all the chips that are on this card. The other objective is to get rid of all one's cards; when a player succeeds in playing his last card, he collects chips from the other players, one for each card still held.

10. I DOUBT IT

This very informal game can be played by three or more. When more than four play, it is best to use two or three decks of cards, all shuffled and dealt as a single deck. The game is usually played with the ace as the lowest and the king as highest card, but players accustomed to the game of Bridge may prefer to play with ace high and two-spot low.

The player at the dealer's left begins play by taking from his hand one, two, three, or four cards, *supposedly* of the same rank, and placing them face down on the table, announcing their number and supposed rank as he does so, saying for example, "Three kings." He is not required to tell the truth about the cards he plays; he may or may not be telling the truth, and the other players must decide which is the case. When any one of the other players wishes to do so, he may call "I doubt it," and if more than one does so the one whose turn to play comes first takes precedence. At this point the cards in question are turned face up. If the doubter is sustained, the player takes the cards back into his own hand; if not, the doubter adds them to his. Whether the first play is doubted or not, the next player takes one to four cards from his hand, places them on the table face down, and announces them as cards *of the next higher rank;* for example, if the first player announces threes, the second player *must* announce fours. To repeat: the second player has no choice, but must call fours whether he has any fours or not. Then the third player announces fives, the next sixes, and so on until kings are called. After kings, the next man calls aces, without delay, the next twos, and so on indefinitely. All these plays and calls must be made in rapid succession and without hesitation except when play is interrupted by a doubter.

Whenever "I doubt it" is called, the cards in question are turned face up and the player or the doubter, whichever one is right, must take *all the cards that have been played* face up by any player and add them to his hand. Scoring is negative only: When any player is rid of all his cards, each other player scores one negative point for each card remaining in his hand. The game continues until one player has three hundred negative points. The one with the fewest points is the winner.

11. TWENTY-NINE

This game can be played by any number from two to eight. A standard deck is used, but cards are removed when necessary to make the total evenly divisible among the players; that is, a full deck is used for two or four players, fifty-one cards for three players, fifty cards for five players, forty-eight cards for six or eight players, and forty-nine cards for seven players. When the number of cards is to be reduced, an appropriate number of ten-spots is discarded.

The player at the dealer's left plays any card face up on the table, calling out its point value as he does so; all picture cards count ten points each, and all other cards their face values. That is, a king, queen, jack, or ten counts ten points, an ace counts one, a five-spot counts five, and so on.

The object of each player is to play a card that will bring the cumulative total to exactly twenty-nine. When one does so he takes the trick (that is, all the cards that have been played), and the next player begins a new series. A player is not permitted to play a card that will bring the total above twenty-nine, and he cannot refuse to play a card that will not bring the total above this number. When one cannot play any card without making the total too large, he says "Pass," and the next man plays. For example, *A*, the first player, plays a six-spot, calling "six"; *B* plays a nine and calls "fifteen"; *C* plays a ten and calls "twenty-five"; *D* plays an ace and calls "twenty-six"; then *E* plays a three, calls "twenty-nine" and takes the trick. Next *F* (or *A* if only five are playing) plays any card to begin a new trick. Each player scores one point for every trick that he takes, and the first to accumulate a prescribed total of points is the winner.

Section II: Move games

12. TICK-TACK-TOE

Tit-tat-to. Naughts and Crosses.

It is probably unnecessary to describe this game, since it must be known to everyone, but it is included nevertheless, because it seems to belong to every collection of games. It is played by two persons using only pencil and paper. One of the players draws a simple diagram consisting of two horizontal lines with two vertical lines crossing them, so as to make nine boxes.

X		O
X	O	
X	O	X

The first player marks an X in any one of the nine spaces, and then the second player marks an 0 in any one of the remaining spaces. They continue to make their marks in turn, the first with X and the second with 0, each trying to get three of his marks in a line—horizontal, vertical, or diagonal. One who gets three in a line is the winner. The two take turns in playing first. A game is not necessarily won by either player, but may result in a draw. In fact, if both play correctly neither can win.

13. MAKING SQUARES

This is a game for two, played with pencil and paper. A chart is made by marking a number of dots on the paper, equally spaced, so that they form a large square made up of a number of equal-sized small ones. A chart of any size can be used, but one with seven dots in each line is suggested to start with. The players take turns, each one drawing a little horizontal or vertical line to connect two adjacent dots. The object of the game is to draw such a line so as to complete a square, and when a player does so he marks his initial in the square. When all squares have been completed, the player with the majority of them to his credit is the winner, and a new game is begun.

Sometimes, when a player completes a square, he *must* take another turn (this may or may not be to his advantage), but it is here recommended that the game be played without this rule.

The chart does not need to be a square; it may be some other kind of rectangle or even an irregular figure made up of several rectangles. The game is best for two players but can be played by three or four, each for himself.

14. NINE MEN'S MORRIS
Mill. Morelles.

This is a very old game that was once widely known. It flourished in England in Elizabethan days, when it was sometimes known as *Ninepenny Morris* and variations were called such names as *Fivepenny Morris* and *Twelve Men's Morris*. It is played very little today, but it has far more than historical interest. It is an excellent game and should be much better known.

Two play the game, each of them using nine men or counters of a distinguishing color. Checkers make perfect men, but many other objects are satisfactory—buttons, bottle tops, golf tees, and the like. The men are placed on the diagram illustrated in Figure 1, being

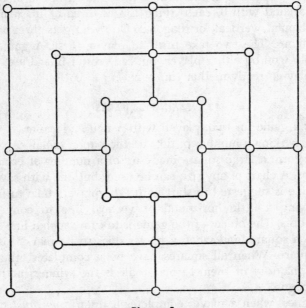

Figure 1.

played only on the twenty-four corners, junctions, and intersections of the lines; the lines themselves have no function except as aids to the eye. The diagram can be made by drawing lines on a sheet of cardboard; however, one that is sold commercially has holes drilled in a board, the men consisting of pegs that are inserted into the holes, and another has hemispherical depressions into which marbles fit.

The ultimate objective of each player is to remove his opponent's men from the board, but to do so one must first get three of his own men in a straight line—therefore the latter is the first objective. To begin the game, the first player places one of his men on any one of the twenty-four spots and then the other player does the same. They continue to place men alternately until all of them are on the board (except for the possible removal of a man as described below).

When all the men have been placed on the board, each player in turn *moves* one of his men, and in so doing, may move the man only along a line and only to the next spot. If at any time, either in placing his men on the board or in moving them, a player succeeds in getting three of his men in one straight line, then he removes an opposing man from the board. In this case he is not permitted to take a man from a row of three unless all of them are in such rows. When a player removes an opposing man, he is said to "pound" the man.

When a player has lost six of his men and is left with only three, his game is changed radically, for now his moves are not restricted as before. He may "jump," that is, he may pick up one of his men and place it *on any spot whatever on the board*, whenever it is his turn to play. Thus the game has three rather distinct stages; placing the men on the board, moving, and jumping. A player wins when he reduces his opponent to two men.

15. BATTLESHIP

Battleship is an excellent game for two players. It includes a considerable element of chance but also provides a surprisingly great opportunity for reasoning. Each player must have two charts, each chart a square made up of one hundred small squares. Each game requires four such charts, and since the charts can be used only once, having to supply the necessary ones for a number of games can kill the desire to play. Fortunately, the difficulty can be overcome rather easily. Some players have a large number of charts run off on a mimeograph or other duplicating machine, but an easier solution for most people is simply to use ordinary cross-section paper, the kind with four or five lines to the inch and no heavy lines. One sheet of such paper will supply a player's needs for several games.

Each of the two players marks off on his cross-section paper two squares, each ten spaces wide and ten spaces high. On each chart he marks the letters *a* to *j* at the heads of the columns and the numbers 1 to 10 at the left of the rows. In this way, each of the one hundred spaces in a chart can be identified by its letter and number; for example, the one at the upper left corner is *a*-1, the one to the right of it is *b*-1, and the one below it is *a*-2. On one of his two charts a player keeps track of his own ships and on the other of the enemy ships.

Each player starts the game with one battleship, two destroyers, and one cruiser. He now marks these ships on his own chart in any places that he chooses; the battleship takes up four adjacent spaces, the cruiser three, and each destroyer two. They may extend horizontally or vertically; some players permit them to extend diagonally, but this seems illogical and is not recommended. It is extremely important that neither player see the chart of the other at any time during the game.

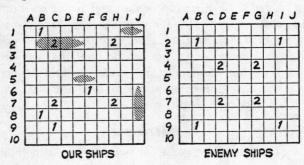

Figure 2.

Now the first player fires four shots at his opponent's ships. He does this by selecting any four spaces and calling out the letter and number for each, such as "*e*-7, *g*-9, *a*-3, *j*-10." The attacker marks the number 1 in each of the appropriate spaces on his second chart, that is, on the one on which he keeps track of the enemy; the enemy does the same thing on his first chart, the one on which he has marked his own ships. After the four shots have been fired and recorded, the defender must tell whether any of his ships have been hit. He does not tell which shot hit, but only the number of hits and the type of vessel struck. For example, he might say, "One hit on my battle-ship," or "One hit on one of my destroyers and one on the cruiser." The attacker must, of course, keep accurate track of his hits on the enemy, for only in this way can he have a basis for logically direct-ing future shots. Now the original defender becomes attacker and fires four shots, these being recorded in the same way as the first four. The two players alternate in firing four shots until one of them succeeds in sinking an enemy ship by having struck every one of the spaces occupied by that ship.

When a ship is sunk, its owner loses one of his four shots and thereafter gets only three at each turn; when he has lost two ships he gets two shots, and so on until either he or his opponent has lost all four of his ships.

16. PYRAMID

This game is played on a checkerboard, each of the two players having ten checkers. The ten checkers are placed on the black squares in the form of a symmetrical pyramid—four in the first row, three in the second, two in the third, and one in the fourth. The men are moved exactly as in the game of checkers, with the very important exception that a man that has been jumped is not removed; the twenty checkers with which the game is started are all on the board at the finish. The object of each player is to get his men to the far side of the board, again in the form of a pyramid; in other words, his pyramid must be in the position originally occupied by the opponent's checkers.

17. TAKE THE LAST

Two players start with a single pile or row of fifteen matches or other convenient objects. The players take turns in removing matches and on any turn may remove one, or two, or three matches. Each tries to force the other to remove the last match.

This perhaps is as much a puzzle as a game, for the first player can figure out a method by which he is sure to win. If, on his first play, he takes two matches and leaves thirteen, then on his second play, no matter what the second player does, he can reduce them to nine, on his third play to five, and on his fourth play to one, thus forcing his opponent to take the last one.

18. MAKE HIM TAKE IT

Two players start with fifteen matches in three piles of three, five, and seven matches respectively. As in Take the Last, the players take turns in removing matches, each trying to force the other to take the last one, but the rules for taking the matches are different. Here, each man on each turn may take matches from only one of the three piles, but he may take as many matches as he wishes, from one to the entire pile. The game can be varied by using piles with different numbers of matches, for example two, three, and five; or three, four, and five.

19. ODD MATCH

This game is similar to the preceding two and is perhaps best of the three. Two players start with fifteen matches in one pile and take turns in removing matches, taking one, two, or three matches at each turn. The player's object is to have the number of matches he removes total *an odd number*. Thus a man wins if he takes seven matches and his opponent eight. It makes no difference which player takes the last match.

20. WORD-SQUARE GAME

Each player has a chart consisting of a large square made up of twenty-five small squares in five rows of five each. One player calls out any letter of the alphabet, and every player writes this letter in one of his small squares, any one that he chooses. Then the second player calls a letter, and all write this letter on their charts. The players call letters in order until twenty-five have been called and then, of course, each player will have his chart completely filled. The object is to locate the letters on the chart in such a way that they will spell words horizontally or vertically (but not diagonally). A player scores one point for each word of three letters or more. Only one word can be counted in any row; that is, words within words or overlapping words, are not counted.

Section III: Dice games

21. CENTENNIAL

This game for two uses three standard dice, each a cube with from one to six spots on its respective faces. The players take turns in throwing all three dice at once, one throw at each turn. Each player's object is to have his throws show one through twelve spots in regular sequence, and then from twelve back to one again. In counting these numbers, a player can consider the spots on a single die and disregard the others, or he can add the spots on any two dice or on all three of them. Furthermore, any die can be counted in any number of different combinations on the same throw. Obviously a player cannot make any progress until he has thrown a one; if there is not a one on his first throw, he passes the dice to the next player and waits for his next turn. As soon as he throws a combination that includes a one, he can, of course, count the one, and often he can go further. For example, a throw of two ones and a five would allow him to count one of the ones and then add the two of them together for his two, the five being of no value. If he should have the good fortune to throw 1-2-4 on his first turn, he could count 1, 2, 3, 4, 5, 6 and 7, all on this one throw.

As soon as one player has made the round trip from one through twelve, and back from twelve through one, he wins.

22. EVEREST

Everest is much like Centennial, but differs in two important respects: (*a*) the numbers can be counted in any order desired and need not be consecutive; (*b*) each die can be counted in only one combination on any throw. Each player must have a double chart, showing the numbers from one through twelve in one column, and from twelve back to one in another; this is necessary because the player will be scoring in both series of numbers at the same time.

The first player rolls three dice and counts the numbers showing, either singly or in combination, on any of the spaces of his chart. For example, if he throws 1-3-5 he can count a one, a three, and a five; or he can count a four and a five, a one and an eight, a three and a six, or a nine. Some of the numbers on the dice may be unusable and be disregarded. It must be remembered that a player can count at any time any of the twenty-four numbers; thus a throw of 1-1-2 could give credit for the one and the two in the ascending series, and the one in the descending one. The winner is the player who first scores all his twenty-four numbers.

23. ACE IN THE POT

This game can be played by two or more. It requires two standard dice and a small supply of chips or other counters. Each player starts the game with a certain number of chips—usually two, but sometimes three or four. The players take turns in making a single throw of the two dice. If a player's roll includes neither a one nor a six, it counts for nothing and the dice are passed to the next player. If either of the dice shows a one, the player must place one of his chips in the pot, that is, in the center of the table; if both the dice show ones, he must place two chips in the pot (provided he has two, otherwise only one). If he rolls a six, he must pass one chip to the player at his left, and if he rolls two sixes he must pass two chips (again provided he has two). If he rolls an ace and a six and has two chips, he pays one to the pot and one to the neighbor, but if he has only one it goes to the pot.

A player who has no chips at all does not roll the dice, but he is not out of the game, because he may receive a chip from the man on his right, and still have a chance to win. The process of throwing the dice and passing chips continues until all chips but one are in the pot. This situation is certain to develop—the only thing that could prevent it would be for one man to have the last two chips and then throw two ones, but in this case the rule provides that he pay only one chip to the pot and keep the other; of course, if he should throw an ace and a six he would pay one chip to the pot and one to his neighbor.

When only one chip is not in the pot, a new phase of the game begins. The holder of the odd chip throws the dice, and this time he throws them, not once, but three times in succession. On these throws aces are disregarded, but any six requires passing the chip to the next man. In other words, the holder of the last chip is winner of the game only if he can make three successive throws of two dice without a single six. If he throws a six and passes the chip, the next man tries the same thing and the process is continued until one player succeeds in making three throws without a six. The first to do so takes all the chips.

24. CRAPS

Craps is best known as a gambling game but it can readily be played without gambling. It is played with two standard dice and, unless actual money is used, requires a supply of chips to be used as counters. Each player starts with a number of chips, which are charged against him, and the dice are assigned, by some chance method, to one of the players who will start the game.

The first player lays out on the table the number of chips that he wishes to risk and these, or possibly only some of them, are matched by one or more of the other players. The man with the dice takes them in one hand, shakes them thoroughly, and rolls them out on the table. Throughout the game the only number that counts for anything is the sum of the spots on the two dice. If this number on the very first roll happens to be either seven or eleven, it is called a "natural," and the roller immediately wins all the chips that have been wagered; that is, he takes all the chips that have been laid on the table. If the first roll happens to be two, three, or twelve, then the roller immediately *loses* all the chips that he has wagered. In either of these cases, the roller makes a new wager and begins again.

If the first roll is none of these numbers, it must, of course, be four, five, six, eight, nine, or ten. Any such number is called a "point," and neither wins nor loses at once; the outcome will be decided by later rolls. After rolling a point, the player continues to shake and roll the dice as many times as required to determine the outcome, and this is determined as soon as he rolls either his point again, or a seven; the former wins for him and the latter loses. It is understood, of course, that while he is trying for his point any number except the point or seven is disregarded, and he may roll the dice an indefinite number of times before making either of these. If a player establishes a point and later wins by rolling the point again before a seven, he keeps the dice and makes a fresh start; but if he rolls a seven while trying for the point, he then loses the amount wagered, and the dice as well. The next player on his left takes the dice and starts as the first player did.

25. GOING TO BOSTON

This is a simple game played with three dice. The first player rolls all three dice at once. He leaves the die with the largest number of points and rolls the other two again; if two or three are equally high, he leaves only one of them. After the second roll, he leaves the better of the two and rolls the other one a third time. His score is the total of the three dice after the three rolls. The other players in turn do the same thing and the one with the highest total is the winner.

26. POKER DICE

Each player in turn rolls five dice at once, hoping to make a combination that would rank high in the game of Poker. After the first roll he may accept the dice as they are or he may roll again, and still a third time. On the second and third rolls he may roll all five dice again, or he may leave any number of them and roll the others in an attempt to improve the combination. The player with the best combination after all have rolled is the winner.

27. COOTIE

Bug. Beetle.

The established name for this game is Cootie, but the supposed inelegance of this word has resulted in such euphemisms as Beetle. Any number can play, but the game is too slow with more than four or five. It is played with a single die, and while a standard die can be used, it is much better with a special one that has no spots on its faces, but letters instead. Such a die can be bought, or one can very easily be made from a block of wood or even a lump of sugar. The letters on the respective faces of the die are B-H-L-E-F-T. Each letter is the initial of one part of the anatomy of an imaginary cootie: *B* for body, *H* for head, *L* for leg, *E* for eye, *F* for feeler, and *T* for tail. If a standard die with spots is used, it will be necessary to let each of the six numbers stand for one of the letters.

The players take turns in rolling the die, one roll for each turn. No one can make any progress until he has rolled a *B* and one who rolls any other letter at his first turn must pass the die to the next player and wait for his second turn, and then possibly for several more turns. When he finally rolls a *B*, he draws an ellipse on a piece of paper to represent the body, and then he gets a second roll on this turn. Now his problem is easier, for he can use an *H* for head, a *T* for tail, or an *L* for leg, all of these being parts that connect directly with the body; an *E* for eye or an *F* for feeler will do him no good, since they cannot be added until the head is in place.

After he has drawn the head, he can use an *E* or an *F*. Thus each player takes his turn and each time that he rolls the initial of a part that he can use he draws this part and takes another roll. He needs in all thirteen parts: a body, a head, a tail, two eyes, and six legs. The game is ended when any player has completed his cootie. This player scores thirteen points and others one point for each part completed.

28. YACHT

Yacht is a more advanced game of the same type as Centennial or Everest. It may appear complicated but actually is not. Although completing a game requires considerable time, it is by no means slow but fascinating from beginning to end. The players take turns in rolling five dice, three rolls at each turn. Each one gets twelve turns. There are twelve different combinations to be rolled, and a player must choose one of these for each of his turns, scoring in proportion to his success. The twelve combinations are these:

1. Ones (the number of ones rolled)
2. Twos (the number of twos rolled)
3. Threes (the number of threes rolled)
4. Fours (the number of fours rolled)
5. Fives (the number of fives rolled)
6. Sixes (the number of sixes rolled)
7. Little straight (1-2-3-4-5)
8. Big straight (2-3-4-5-6)
9. Full house (three of one kind and two of another)
10. Four of a kind (four of any one number)
11. Choice (no requirement)
12. Yacht (five of any one number)

At each turn, the player rolls five standard dice and then, before he takes the other two rolls to which he is entitled, chooses one of the twelve combinations; this must be one that he has not chosen before, because he gets only one chance at each combination and must dispose of all twelve in twelve innings. This choice is the most important element in the game, and a player's cleverness or good luck in making it is the chief factor in determining his success. This is a good place to point out that the score for any combination is the total of all the spots in the combination, so that four twos score eight points, but four fives score twenty points. This fact requires a player to choose repeatedly between taking a sure but small score and trying for a larger one with the chance of no score at all.

Having rolled the dice once and chosen a combination, the player now leaves any of the dice with which he is satisfied and rolls the others again; after the second roll he again leaves as many dice as he thinks wise and rolls the others. Of course it is always possible that he will be satisfied after the first or second roll and not take any more. Suppose, for example, that a player rolls 1-1-1-2-2. He could choose to play for ones, in which case he would leave the three ones that he has already, and roll the other dice in the hope of getting another one or possibly two of them. If he gets another one on his second trial, he rolls only the remaining die on the third; otherwise he rolls both of them again on the third trial. Thus he is sure to get three points for ones and might get four or five. Suppose, however, that he elects to try for four-of-a-kind; in this case he again leaves the ones and takes two more rolls with the other dice. He may have bad luck and not get another one, in which case he must score zero for four-of-a-kind. Even if he is successful he scores only four points for four ones, and this is a very unsatisfactory score in view of the fact that he has a possibility of twenty-four points for making his four-of-a-kind with sixes. It should not be hard for him to elect the ones on this roll and plan to try for four-of-a-kind later, but many times the choice is not so easy to make.

When a player elects "Choice," he then rolls three times as usual, and scores the total value of the spots regardless of what they are. In other words, no combination at all is required, and the player's only objective is to make the six sets of spots add up as high as possible. The game continues until every player has had twelve innings; then the scores are totaled and compared.

29. HEARTS DICE

In its original form, this game is played with six special dice, each with the letters *H-E-A-R-T-S* on its respective faces. The players take turns in making one roll with all six dice and score as follows: for the letter *H*, 5 points; for *H-E*, 10 points; for *H-E-A*, 15; for *H-E-A-R*, 20; for *H-E-A-R-T*, 25; and for *H-E-A-R-T-S*, 35 points. When doubles are thrown, that is, two letters of the same kind, only one of them counts. Triples also are disregarded, except three *H*'s. One who rolls three *H*'s loses all his score up to that point and goes back to zero. Thus, if a player rolls *H-H-A-R-T-S*, he scores only five points for the *H*; if he rolls *H-E-R-T-T-S* he scores ten for the *H-E*; if he rolls *E-A-R-T-T-S* he scores zero.

This game can be played with standard dice simply by substituting the numbers 1 to 6 for the letters.

Part Two

ACTIVE GAMES, CONTESTS, AND STUNTS

Chapter 11

RACES AND RELAYS

As USED HERE, THE WORD "RACE" APPLIES TO ANY CONTEST FOR SPEED, whether speed in running or in some other form of activity. Races in general are likely to be contests in running or some other kind of locomotion, but most of the races described in this book, being restricted to those suitable for indoor use, are based on activities other than locomotion.

Contrary to usual practice, relay races are not separated here from simple races. After all, most relay races are identical with simple races, except that the players form teams and the members of each team take turns in performing the same activity. A separate listing of both kinds of race would require describing them twice. Accordingly, most of the races are described with the understanding that they can be conducted in either form. It will be noted if a race is recommended for only one form or if it requires some special treatment.

Section 1: Locomotion races

These races require, of course, a starting line and a finish line. Rather than having a line at each end of the room, it is usually better to use the turning-post method: A line at one end of the room serves both for start and for finish. Near the far end of the room there is an object of some sort—a chair, a pile of books, or the like—around which each contestant must run. That is, each contestant runs from the line, to and around the object, and back to the line again.

In a relay race, each team lines up in single file behind the line. At the starting signal, the man at the head of each team runs as in the simple race; when he crosses the line on his return trip, he touches the next man on his team, who runs as he did. When the last man of the team has completed his run, the race is completed.

1. PAPER RACE

Each contestant has two pieces of cardboard, or two newspapers, each folded twice. He places the papers on the floor and steps on them, then shifts the papers and advances. He must manipulate the papers so as to run to the turn and back stepping only on the papers.

2. SIR WALTER RALEIGH RACE

This is the Paper Race adapted to couples, each competing couple consisting of a boy and a girl. The boy has the two pieces of paper, which he places on the floor for the girl to walk on. She is not permitted to handle the papers herself, but must travel to the turn and back, stepping only on the papers.

3. BALLOON-FANNING RACE

Each contestant has an ordinary cardboard or palm-leaf fan and an inflated toy balloon. He drives the balloon to the turn and back, entirely by fanning it; he must not touch the balloon with the fan or with any part of his body.

4. FEATHER-FANNING RACE

Each contestant has a small feather and a fan. He drives the feather to the turn and back, entirely by fanning it. He is required to drive it over a small section of the line at the finish. A more difficult requirement is sometimes used—making the feather come to rest in a plate on the finish line.

A sheet of tissue paper, about four inches square, can be used instead of a feather.

5. BROOM-AND-BALLOON RACE

Each contestant has an inflated toy balloon and an ordinary broom. He drives the balloon with the broom, to the turn and back. In the relay form, it is well to have two brooms for each team, so that the runner who is waiting for his turn will have a broom ready.

6. BROOM-AND-PAPER RACE

Each man has an ordinary broom and a full-sized ($8\frac{1}{2} \times 11$) sheet of paper. The paper is placed flat on the floor, and the contestant is required to drive it with the broom, sweeping it to the turn and back.

7. POTATO ROLL

Each contestant has a potato, an apple, or, perhaps best of all, a lemon, and an ordinary dull-edged table knife. Touching the potato only with the knife, he pushes it to the turn and back. For this race, the turn should be not more than eight feet from the starting line.

8. HEAD-BALANCE RACE

Each contestant balances a book, an apple, a board, or some other object on his head. Any suitable object can be used, but all contestants must have the same kind. He walks or runs to the turn and back with the object balanced on his head and, of course, without touching it with his hands. If the object falls it may be replaced, provided the contestant does not advance while replacing it.

9. CANDLE RACE

This race involves the danger of fire, and the less serious danger of damage to rugs, furniture, or clothing from dripping wax. It must not be used except where these dangers can be eliminated. Each contestant stands at the starting line holding a lighted candle and runs with it to the turn and back. Usually, a man whose candle goes out is eliminated, but sometimes each runner is permitted to carry matches to relight his candle.

10. COUPLE CANDLE-RACE

This is a two-man form of the Candle Race, each contestant being a couple, usually a boy and a girl. The boy stands at one end of the room with a lighted candle, and the girl at the other end with an unlighted one. The boy runs to the girl, lights her candle from his, and then extinguishes his. As soon as her candle is lighted, the girl runs back to the other end and across the finish line. The race may be varied to require the girl to turn, run back to the boy, and relight his candle, the boy then running to the other end of the room.

11. FEATHER RACE

Each contestant has a paper plate on which are three or four small fluffy feathers. Holding the plate and without touching the feathers, he runs to the turn and back. The first to finish without losing a feather is the winner.

12. SUGAR-LUMP RACE

Each contestant runs to the turn and back while balancing a lump of sugar on his nose.

13. KNIFE-AND-PEANUT RACE

Each man runs while carrying a peanut (in the shell) or similar small object on the blade of a dull table knife.

14. EGG-AND-SPOON RACE

Each man stands at the starting line holding an empty spoon. On the floor at the turn is a wooden egg. He runs to the turn, picks up the egg in the spoon, touching it only with the spoon, and runs back.

15. PINGPONG RACE

This is another race for two-man teams. The two stand behind the starting line, face to face, each with both hands on the other's shoulders, holding a table-tennis (pingpong) ball between their foreheads. Keeping the ball in this position, they run to the turn and back. The ball, of course, must not be touched except with the forehead.

Section II: Eating, chewing, and blowing races

16. CHEW THE STRING

Each contestant has a piece of string about five feet long, one end fastened to some firm object and the other end in his mouth. At a signal, he starts to chew on the string so as to get all of it into his mouth. The first one to get all his string into his mouth is the winner

17. PARTNER CHEW-THE-STRING

In this form of Chew the String the contestants are paired off. Each pair has a single piece of string about eight feet long, with a piece of candy tied in the middle; each player takes one end of the string in his mouth. At a signal, they both begin to chew the string into their mouths and continue until one or the other gets to the candy and takes it into his mouth. The first pair to do this wins.

18. CHEWING TUG-OF-WAR

This is a contest for two players only. To accommodate a larger number of players, several different contests will have to go on simultaneously. A piece of candy is tied to the middle of a piece of string eight to ten feet long, and each of the two contestants takes one end of the string in his mouth. At a signal each, with hands held behind his back, begins to chew the string into his mouth in an attempt to get to the candy. The one who gets the candy is the winner.

19. CRACKER RACE

Each contestant has two salted crackers. They race to see who can be first to eat his crackers and then give a distinctly audible whistle.

20. BALLOON BUST

Each contestant has an uninflated toy balloon. At a signal, all begin to inflate their balloons by blowing into them, and they continue blowing until the balloons burst. The first to burst his balloon is the winner.

Section III: Clothing races

21. ELOPEMENT RACE

This is a race for boy-and-girl pairs. A closed umbrella and a closed suitcase, containing various articles of men's and women's clothing and accessories, are placed on the floor a few feet in front of each couple. Any articles will do, provided they can be put on over the players' regular clothing: hats, gloves, coats, bathrobes, galoshes, and so on. At the starting signal, each pair rushes to its suitcase, opens it, puts on all the clothing, and raises the umbrella. Leaving the suitcase where it is, they run to the turn and back, then take off all the clothing, replace it in the suitcase, close the suitcase, and close the umbrella. Then they run back to the finish line.

22. NECKTIE-AND-APRON RACE

This is another race for boy-and-girl pairs. The two partners stand facing each other, the boy holding an apron and the girl a necktie.

At the starting signal, the boy proceeds to tie the apron on the girl, and the girl to tie the necktie on the boy at the same time. The first couple to complete both jobs acceptably is the winner.

23. CLOTHES-HANGING RACE

This race, also for couples, requires something that will serve as a clothesline. It may be a short section of rope for each pair, or a longer section to be used by all. Each couple stands at the starting line with various articles of clothing and a few clothespins. They run from the start to the clothesline, fasten the articles to it with two clothespins for each, and run back to the start.

24. PILLOW-CASE RACE

Several couples compete for speed in casing and uncasing a pillow. Each couple stands side by side, the boy holding a pillow in a case. At the signal, the boy takes the pillow out of the case and hands it to the girl, keeping the case himself. The girls slips the pillow into the case while the boy holds it. Then the girl takes the pillow out of the case and the boy puts it back while the girl holds the case.

25. COAT-AND-HAT RELAY

The players are divided into relay teams, and each team has one coat and one hat. At a signal, the first man on each team puts the coat on and buttons it completely, then puts the hat on. Then he unbuttons the coat and takes it off, takes off the hat, and hands both coat and hat to the next member of his team. When the last man of the team has taken the coat and hat off and set them down, the team has completed the race; the first team to do so wins.

Section IV: Object-manipulation races

GROUP A: BEAN RACES

The name "Bean Races" is applied to contests of speed in which players transfer or otherwise handle dried beans or similar small objects, such as grains of rice or corn.

26. BEAN CARRY

Each contestant has a table knife and two cups, one cup empty and the other containing about six dried beans. Using the knife only and never touching the beans with his hands, the contestant transfers the beans one at a time from one cup to the other.

27. BEAN-AND-STRAW RACE

As in Bean Carry, each contestant has several beans in one cup, and he is required to transfer them one at a time to another cup. Instead of a knife he has a soda straw, and he picks up and carries each bean by inhaling through the straw.

28. RICE PICKING

Each contestant has two saucers or other flat dishes, placed about a foot apart, one empty and the other containing a number of grains of uncooked rice. He has two knitting needles, toothpicks, or other sticks that might be considered substitutes for chopsticks. Using these sticks only, he transfers the grains of rice, one at a time, from one dish to the other.

29. BEAN-AND-BOTTLE RACE

Each contestant has a small-necked bottle. A six-ounce soft drink bottle will do, but a smaller one is better. He also has a bowl containing enough beans to fill, or almost fill, the bottle. He gets the beans into the bottle by any method that he cares to use. The first man to get all his beans into the bottle is the winner, provided he does not spill a single bean from the bowl. One who spills a bean is eliminated from the contest.

30. BLACK-BEAN CONTEST

Each contestant has a bowl containing about a half-pint of dried beans, about two-thirds of them white and one-third black. He picks out the black beans, using any method desired, and drops them into a cup. A limited time is allowed, and the player who gets most beans into his cup in the allotted time is the winner.

31. BEAN EXTRACTING

Each contestant has a cup containing several beans in one hand, a teaspoon in the other, and an empty cup on top of his head. While looking into a mirror, he transfers the beans one at a time, using only the spoon, from the cup in his hand to the one on his head. The player who completes the transfer in the shortest time, without spilling a bean, is the winner.

32. FEED-THE-NEIGHBOR RELAY

Players form relay teams, each team sitting or standing in a straight line. Every player has one toothpick, and the first man on each team has a small bowl of raisins. At a signal, each man with a bowl spears three raisins with his toothpick and feeds them, all at once, to the next man on his team. This man, as soon as he has the raisins in his mouth, takes the bowl, spears three raisins, and feeds them to the third man. The race continues until the man at the far end of the row has three raisins in his mouth; then he takes the bowl and runs back to the other end of the line, where he spears three raisins and feeds them to the first man. The first team to get the three raisins into the mouth of its first man is the winner.

33. RICE-PICKING RELAY

Players form relay teams, each team in a straight line and preferably seated at a table. Every man has two toothpicks, and the first man on each team has a small bowl of uncooked rice. The man with the bowl, using his toothpicks only, takes a single grain of rice from the bowl and places it on the table or holds it in his hand; he then hands the bowl to the next man on his team. This man, and every other man in turn, takes a grain from the bowl and hands the bowl on, until the last man on the team has removed his grain. The first team to complete the whole process is the winner.

Group B: Manipulate Cards, Books, and Papers

34. DEUCE-TO-ACE RACE

The contestants sit at tables, each with a complete deck of playing cards, well shuffled. At a signal, each player proceeds to arrange his cards by suit and rank; that is, the cards are to be made into a single pile running from deuce up to ace in any one suit, then from deuce to ace in a second suit, a third, and the fourth. The first to arrange his cards in this way and place the deck on the table is the winner.

This contest can be modified for teams of four, each team having one deck. In this case, each member of a team arranges one suit.

35. DEUCE-TO-ACE RELAY

Players form relay teams, each team with one well-shuffled deck of cards. A definite order for all fifty-two cards must be established, beginning from the two of clubs up to the ace, then from the two to the ace of diamonds, the same with hearts, and finally ending with the ace of spades. At a signal, the first player of each team finds the first card, that is the two of clubs, and then hands the remainder of the deck to the next man on his team. This man finds and removes the second card and hands the deck to the third member of the team. After the last member of the team has removed his card, he hands the remainder of the deck to the first one and the team continues until all cards have been removed. The first team to complete the entire process is the winner.

In a variation of the game, the first player removes the four two's, the next player the four three's, and so on.

36. NEWSPAPER SHUFFLING

This contest requires some preparation, but it is more than worth the trouble. A supply of newspapers must be provided, one complete paper for each player. It is best that all the papers be identical, but this is not necessary if they are of the same size and have the same number of pages. Each paper must be taken apart and its sections rearranged so that the page numbers are completely confused, but all papers must have the pages in the same order.. The players sit in a circle on chairs placed as close together as possible, so that the amount of elbow room is very small. Each player is given a copy of the mixed-up newspaper and is instructed to restore its pages to their normal order. With the handicap of the close quarters, the players will find this a difficult assignment, but the first to get the job done is the winner.

37. BIBLE RACE

This race requires a copy of the Bible for each contestant. If not enough Bibles are available, then two or more players can work as a team with a single Bible. A Bible verse is announced, and all race to see who can first find it, and the one who does so is the winner.

38. TELEPHONE-DIRECTORY RELAY

Players are divided into relay teams, and each team is given a copy of a telephone directory, all directories being identical. The leader prepares in advance identical lists of page numbers, each accompanied by another number, the latter not greater than ten. Each team is given one of the lists. At a signal, the first player of each team opens his directory to the page indicated by the first number on the list, and in the right-hand column of this page he counts down the entries as far as indicated by the small number that accompanies the page number. Having found the indicated entry, he writes its telephone number on a sheet of paper, then hands list, directory, and sheet of paper to the second man on his team. Proceeding in the same way, the second man finds the second telephone number and writes it down, and the same process is repeated for the other numbers by the other players. This is continued until every player has found and written down a telephone number. The first team to produce a complete and accurate list is the winner.

39. CLIPPING RELAY

The leader selects in advance a number of items from a newspaper and lists them by headline or by some descriptive phrase such as "Story of Smathers Wedding," or "Advertisement of Perkins Grocery Store." He makes a number of copies of this list and gives one to each team, together with a copy of the paper and a pair of scissors. At a signal, the first member of each team finds the first item and clips it out of the paper. He hands the paper and scissors to the next man on his team, who finds and clips the second item, and so on, until all the items have been clipped. The first team to make a complete collection of the clippings is the winner.

GROUP C: MANIPULATE NEEDLES OR SCISSORS

40. THREADNEEDLE RACE

Each contestant runs a few steps to a chair or table on which are a spool of thread and a needle. He breaks off a length of thread, threads the needle, lays it on the table or chair, and runs back to the starting line. In the relay form of this contest, each team has one spool of thread and a needle for each player.

41. PATCHING CONTEST

Each contestant has a threaded needle, a cloth patch six inches square, and a larger piece of cloth. He must sew the patch to the larger cloth, using fifty stitches in doing so. The first one to finish wins.

42. BUTTON-SEWING RACE

Each contestant must thread a needle and then sew a button to a piece of cloth. The first to finish is the winner.

43. THREAD AND TIE

This is a contest for teams of two, each team consisting of a man and a woman. The man wears a shirt with a collar but no necktie. He holds a needle and a length of thread, and his partner holds a necktie. The woman must tie the necktie on the man, and the man must thread the needle. The two jobs may be done at the same time, or in order, but must be completed. The first couple to get both jobs done is the winner.

44. CUT THE TAPE

Each contestant has a pair of scissors and a piece of dressmaker's tape, eight or nine feet long. He cuts the tape from end to end to make two narrow strips. Anyone who cuts to the edge of his tape is eliminated. No tearing is permitted, of course.

GROUP D: MANIPULATE STRINGS AND KNOTS

45. WIND THE STRING

Each player has a piece of string twelve or more feet long, one end tied to his index finger, the other to some fixed object. At a signal, he wraps the string around the finger to which it is tied, until he comes to the other end. The first to complete winding his string is the winner.

46. WASHER RELAY

The first man of each team has a piece of cord about two feet long, and a supply of small metal washers, one more than the number of players on his team. Before the race starts, he ties one of the washers to the end of the string, to keep the others from falling off. At the starting signal, he slips one of the washers onto the string, and immediately hands the string and the remaining washers to the second man on his team. Each man in turn adds a washer until all of them are on the string. The last man strings the last washer and then ties the two ends of the string together.

47. BEAD-STRINGING RELAY

This is the same as Washer Relay, except that the players string beads instead of washers. A small box or basket, containing the beads for each team, is passed from one player to the next. A good variation is to have beads of different colors mixed in the box and to require that the beads be strung in a prescribed sequence of colors.

48. NECKTIE RELAY

The first man of each team has a necktie. He wraps the tie about the neck of the next man and ties a standard four-in-hand knot. The second man unties the knot, removes the tie, and ties it on the third, and so on to the last man, who ties it on the first man. The race is finished when the tie is properly tied on the first man.

49. PAPER-CLIP RELAY

The first man of each team has two paper clips, and every other man has one. At a signal, the first man joins his two clips to start a chain and hands them to the second man. The second man adds his clip to the chain and hands it to the third, and so on until all the clips are in one chain. The last man then carries or throws the chain to the first one, and the latter removes one of the clips. He hands the chain to the second man, who removes a clip and passes it on.

The last man will receive a chain of two clips, from which he removes one to end the race.

50. KNOT-TIE RELAY

The first man of each team has a rather long piece of clothesline or some other kind of rope. A particular knot is specified, one that can be tied in a single rope. At a signal, the first man ties the specified knot and hands the rope to the second, who does the same. The process is continued until every man has tied a knot in the rope. The knot most commonly used is the "bowline."

51. CHAIN-KNOT RELAY

Every man except the last must have a short piece of rope about two feet long. The first man of each team ties his rope to that of the second, using whatever knot is specified. The second man ties the second to the third, and so on until the next-to-last man ties the last piece of rope to the chain. Then the last man takes the chain and ties the two ends together to complete the race.

52. SLIP-KNOT RELAY

Each team needs some cord or light rope of considerable length. The team should form a circle. The first man forms a slip knot near one end of the rope, slips the loop of the knot over the wrist of the second man, and pulls it tight. The second man forms a similar loop and tightens it about the wrist of the third, and so on to the last man, who ties his knot to the wrist of the first man, thus completing the process of tying all the members of the team together.

GROUP E: OTHER MANIPULATION RACES

53. CANDLE-LIGHTING RACE

Two men kneel facing each other. Each man holds a candle in his right hand, one candle lit, the other not. Each of the two holds his left foot in his left hand and raises his left leg clear of the floor so as to balance himself on his right knee and leg only. While both men are in this position, they light one candle from the other. Several pairs compete for the shortest time required to light the candle. The same idea is the basis of a stunt called Candle Balance. (See Chapter 13.)

54. BOTTLE-BALANCE RACE

The contestant sits on a bottle that is flat on the floor parallel with his legs. His legs are extended straight forward, and then one leg is crossed over the other so that he is balanced on the bottle and one heel. While in this position, he threads a needle, trying to better the time required for others to do so. Instead of threading a needle, he may be required to write his name, light a cigarette, or perform some other suitable action. The same idea is the basis of a stunt called Bottle Balance. (See Chapter 13.)

55. BOTTOMS-UP RELAY

Each team has a chair on the seat of which three milk bottles stand upright. At a signal, the first man transfers the bottles one at a time, using one hand only, to an upside down stand on the floor. The second man transfers them back to the chair seat, and so on.

56. SHIFT-THE-BOTTLE RELAY

The teams form in parallel single files behind a starting line. A few feet in front of the line each team has three bottles standing upright on the floor inside a circle about two feet in diameter. A similar circle is tangent to, or close by, the first. At the starting signal, the first man rushes to his bottles and, with one hand only, transfers them from the first circle to the second. He then runs back to touch the second man, who transfers the bottles, one at a time, back to their original circle. This continues, each man shifting the bottles to the other circle, until all have run.

This race needs some improvising. In the first place, bottles that are easily upset should be used, because the requirement that they remain upright adds to the fun of the race. In the second place, there is often a problem about marking the circles on the floor. Any well-marked areas will do, but it may be more desirable to use sheets of cardboard or some other material.

57. BALL-AND-BOTTLE RELAY

Each team has six empty, small-necked bottles, three of them with a golf ball resting on top. The first man transfers the balls one at a time, with one hand only, to the tops of the second group of bottles and then touches the second man, who moves them back to the original bottles, and so on until all have shifted the balls.

58. BOTTLE-FILLING RACE

Each contestant has a bucket of water on the floor, and an empty bottle placed a few feet away. He has an empty tin cup in his hand. At a signal, he dips water from the bucket with the tin cup, dashes to the bottle, and pours the water into the bottle. Then he rushes back for more water, continuing to carry water and to pour it into the bottle until the bottle is full. The first to fill his bottle is the winner.

Section V: Object-passing relays

GROUP A: FREE-STYLE PASSING

59. HURRY-HURRY RELAY

Each team stands in line, side by side. A pile of various objects is on the floor at one end of the line. It makes no difference what these objects are—the more they vary the better—but the piles for all teams should be the same. Books, pans, pencils, old hats, newspapers, and anything else might be used. At a signal, the man next to the pile picks up any one of the objects and hands it to the second man, and it is passed on from one to the next until it reaches the last man, who must place it on the floor at the far end of the line. As soon as the first man is rid of the first object he starts the second, then the third, and so on, following one object with another as rapidly as possible. When the last object has been passed and the whole pile thus transferred from one end of the team to the other, the race is at an end. It is often better to require each player to keep one hand behind his back while handling the objects.

60. DINNER-TABLE RELAY

This is essentially the same race as the preceding one, except that it is played by people sitting at tables. With one long table, those on one side can compete against those on the other. A collection of pieces of china, silverware, napkins and other small articles is passed, one at a time, from one end of the table to the other, as in the Hurry-Hurry Relay. With two or more tables, those at each table form a team, and in this case the objects are passed completely around the table.

61. TEN TRIPS

This is another dinner-table race. It requires at least two tables of people, but the tables need not be very large. At each table a single object, usually a napkin, is started at a designated place and passed from person to person all around the table. When it returns to the man who started it, he calls "One" and starts it on a second round. It is passed around the table ten times, the first man calling aloud each time it completes a trip. The first table to complete the ten trips is the winner.

62. RED-AND-WHITE RELAY

This race is also good for the dinner table but can be played elsewhere as well. Each team sits or stands in line, and each end man holds a small box. Each box contains fifteen or twenty toothpicks or other small objects, red ones in one box, white in the other. At the signal, the two players at the ends of each team start at the same time, each passing toothpicks one at a time. They are handed from one man to the next until all have been shifted from one box to another. The crossing of the two groups of toothpicks as they travel in opposite directions adds a new and interesting element to this race.

GROUP B: BALANCE PASSING

63. POTATO-AND-SPOON RELAY

Each team sits or stands in a line. The first man has a potato, a tennis ball, or similar object balanced in the bowl of a spoon. The players, each using one hand only, pass the spoon from one end of the line to the other without dropping the potato. The race may be varied by having each team form a circle and pass the spoon around the circle two or three times.

64. ARCH-PASS RELAY

Each team sits on the floor in single file. The front man on each team has a saucer containing several marbles or any other small objects that will roll off easily. The players pass this dish overhead backward from man to man until it reaches the rear. The first team to get the dish to the rear without spilling a marble is the winner.

65. OVERHEAD SUGAR RELAY

Each team stands in single file. The front man has a playing card with several lumps of sugar balanced on it. The card is passed backward overhead, from man to man, until it reaches the rear.

66. CORNMEAL-PASSING RELAY

Each team stands or sits in a line, all members facing the same way. A bowl of cornmeal is placed at one end of the line and an empty vessel of some sort at the other. The man standing next to the cornmeal has from four to six teaspoons. At the starting signal, this man fills one of his spoons with cornmeal and starts the spoon down the line, each man handing it to the next; when the last man receives the spoon he dumps the cornmeal into the empty vessel. As soon as the first man passes the first spoon he fills and starts the second, then the third, and the others in turn. As soon as the man at the other end has emptied a spoon, he starts it back and it is handed from man to man just as the filled spoon was. Thus, when the race is underway, there is a continuous stream of filled spoons going one way and of empty ones going the other. After an appropriate time has elapsed, the amounts of cornmeal transferred are compared. There is no penalty for spilling cornmeal, only credit for the amount that reaches the second vessel.

GROUP C: PUT-AND-TAKE RELAYS

A put-and-take relay is one in which objects are passed along, but instead of being handed directly from man to man, they are put down or placed somewhere by one man and then picked up by the next.

67. HANDFUL RELAY

Each team stands in a line. A pile of clothespins or similar articles —so many that a person will have some difficulty picking them all up at once in his two hands—is on the floor at one end of the line. At the signal, the man nearest the clothespins picks them all up at once and drops them to the floor in front of the next man. The latter picks them all up and drops them in front of the third man. Each player picks up the clothespins and drops them again until the last man has dropped them at the far end of the line.

68. CLOTHESPIN RELAY

Each team stands in line. The man at one end has five spring-type clothespins. At the signal, he attaches these to the fingers of the next man, one on each finger of the nearer hand. As soon as they are all in place, the second man removes them and attaches them to the hand of the next and so on until they are on the hand of the last man. This is the end of the race as it is usually conducted, but it is better to continue until the last man has attached the clothespins to the hand of the first man. The simplest way to do this is for the team to form in a circle; if the team is in a straight line the last man may run back to the first man and then attach the pins.

69. PENCIL RELAY

Card-Passing Relay

Each team stands in line, the man at one end holding four pencils. He places the pencils one at a time between fingers of the next man; that is, one pencil between the thumb and forefinger, another between the first and second fingers, and so on. As soon as the pencils are in place, the second man removes them and places them between fingers of the third man. He must place them one at a time but may remove them as he desires. The pencils are passed thus from man to man until they reach the end of the line.

Instead of pencils, playing cards may be used, or any other small objects that can be gripped with the fingers.

70. DROP-AND-PICK RELAY

Each team stands or sits in a line. A collection of miscellaneous small objects is at one end of the line: buttons, spools, coins, marbles, or anything else small enough to fit into the cupped hands of a player. Each second player forms a cup by holding his two hands together. The man nearest the objects picks them up one at a time and drops them into the cupped hands of the one next to him. The third man picks the objects from the hands of the second and drops them into the hands of the fourth, and so on. Thus, only the odd numbers handle the objects, and the even furnish the cups. The objects are passed one after another, each passer taking the next object as soon as possible.

GROUP D: OTHER HANDING RELAYS

71. HANDCLASP RELAY

Each team stands in line, each man grasping the hands of his two neighbors. At each end of the line is a chair, one of them with ten peanuts (in the shells) on it. The peanuts are passed, one at a time, from man to man until they are all transferred to the chair at the far end of the line. The passing must be done with the clasped hands, the hands being kept joined from the beginning to the end.

72. RING-ON-THE-STRING RELAY

Each team, standing or sitting in a circle, has a long piece of cord on which all the players hold both hands. An object is placed on the string—a ring or safety pin will do, but a larger object such as a jar rubber is probably better. The object is passed from man to man entirely around the circle and then around a second and a third time. The first team to pass the object around three times is the winner.

73. BALL-OF-STRING RELAY

Each team stands or sits in a circle, one member of the team holding a ball of cord. He ties the loose end of the cord to one of his fingers and then, at a signal, passes the ball to the next man, unwinding the necessary amount of cord. The ball is passed from man to man until it comes back to the one who started it, and each player has at least one hand on the cord. When the first man has recovered the ball of string, he gives the cord one or more turns around the ball and passes it back to the man who handed it to him; that is, he starts it in the reverse direction. Each man must take the ball in his hand and give the string at least one turn around the ball. The race is finished when the ball is back in the hands of the one who started it, with all the string rewound.

74. WRAPAROUND RELAY

Each team stands or sits in a circle, one member of the team holding a ball of string with the loose end tied to his finger. At the starting signal, the man with the string wraps it once around his body, unwinding as much as required, and passes the ball to the next man. This man also wraps the string around his body and passes the ball along. Each man in turn wraps the string around himself and hands the ball to the next, until the ball is in the hands of the one who first held it. He then starts the ball in the reverse direction. Each man in turn unwraps the string that is around his body, winds it on the ball, then passes it along. This continues until the ball, with all string rewound, is back in the hands of the first man.

GROUP E: NO-HANDS PASSING RELAYS

In the relays of this group, objects are passed from man to man, but here the objects are passed in some way other than by hand.

75. MATCH-BOX RELAY

Each team stands in a circle. The first man slips the cover from a safety-match box over his nose. At the starting signal, the box cover must be transferred to the nose of the next man, without the use of hands by either player. It is passed from the second man to the third, and so on until the last man transfers it to the nose of the first, thus completing the race. If the box falls, it may be picked up with the hands and replaced on the nose before the transfer to the next man is resumed.

76. LIP-AND-CARD RELAY

Each team stands in a circle, the first player holding a playing card between his upper lip and nose. The card is passed from man to man around the circle until it is received by the one who started it. The card must, of course, be passed without the use of hands, but if it falls it may be replaced with the hands.

77. INHALE RELAY

The first man on each team has a cup with several dried navy beans in it; each of the others has an empty cup. Every man, including the first one, has a soda straw. By inhaling through his straw, the first man removes a bean from his own cup and drops it into that of the next man; he then does the same with the other beans, taking them one at a time as rapidly as possible. Each man takes the beans from his cup and passes them along, always by inhaling through the straw. This is continued until all the beans have been transferred to the end of the line or around the circle.

This relay is best conducted where the players can sit at a table. It is better if they form a circle (or rectangle) so that the beans can go around and finish in the cup of the starter. There is no reason why players should not sit on the floor.

Other objects can be substituted for the beans. Small pieces of paper or cardboard are satisfactory, but if they are to be used, some experimenting should be done with them beforehand.

78. PASS-THE-ORANGE RELAY

Each team sits in a straight line, the members very close together. The man at one end holds an orange on top of his feet. At the signal, the orange is rolled from one end of the line to the other along the tops of the players' feet. If the orange gets away it must be recovered, and replaced, using only the feet.

79. RING-AND-TOOTHPICK RELAY

Each man has a toothpick projecting from his mouth, and the first man of each team has a small ring of some sort on his toothpick. One of the common doughnut-shaped mints is very good for the purpose. Without the use of hands, the players pass the ring from one toothpick to the next until it has reached the last man.

80. FRESH-EGG RELAY

Each man has the handle of a teaspoon in his mouth. The first man has an egg or a substitute object in the bowl of his spoon. A hard-boiled egg, a rubber egg, or something similar is best. The egg is passed from spoon to spoon without the use of the hands. If it falls it can be replaced by hand.

Section VI: Miscellaneous relays

81. CHAIR RELAY

No definite formation is needed for this race, but since each man must take his turn the members of each team should stand in some sort of line. Each team has a folded chair lying on the floor. At the signal, the first man picks up the chair, unfolds it, and sets it on the floor; then he sits on the chair, raises both feet from the floor, and clicks his heels together; finally he stands, folds the chair, and lays it on the floor again, after which he touches the second man on his team. This man, as soon as he is touched, repeats the whole performance, and touches the third, and so on until every man has gone through the process and the chair is lying folded on the floor.

82. BUCKET RELAY

This is simply the Chair Relay with a few added complications. As before, each team has a folded chair lying on the floor, but it also has a bucket with a lid on top and a whistle inside, and a folded umbrella lying on the floor beside the chair. Each man in turn sets up the chair and sits on it; then he opens the umbrella and holds it over his head; next he opens the bucket, removes the whistle, and blows it; he replaces the whistle and the cover of the bucket, closes the umbrella, and replaces it on the floor; folds the chair and lays it on the floor, and finally touches the next man.

83. THROUGH-THE-HOOP RELAY

Each team has a hoop large enough to be passed over the body of a man. A rattan hoop is best, but a wooden barrel hoop is most often used; some other kinds that might be available will serve as well. At the starting signal, the hoop is lying on the floor. The first man picks it up and passes it entirely over his body in either direction, that is, either from head to foot or from foot to head; he then drops the hoop to the floor. Each man in turn picks up the hoop, passes it over his body, and drops it to the floor. When the last man has dropped the hoop, the race is ended.

84. SITTING THROUGH-THE-HOOP RELAY

This relay is somewhat strenuous for some occasions. All players sit on the floor. The first man of each team has a hoop, and at the signal he passes the hoop over his body in either direction without standing. Each in turn receives the hoop, passes it over his body, and hands it to the next man.

85. RUBBER-BAND RELAY

A large rubber band that can be passed over the body of a player is required for each team. Such a band can be cut from an inner tube. Each man in turn takes the band, passes it over his body in either direction, and hands it to the next man.

Chapter 12

MISSILE GAMES AND CONTESTS

THE ACTIVITIES OF THIS CHAPTER ARE THOSE IN WHICH OBJECTS ARE thrown, or otherwise propelled, either for distance or for accuracy. Many of them demand too much action and too much space to be played in a living room, but are especially suitable for a basement recreation room.

Section I: Contests for distance

1. BALLOON THROW

Contestants take turns in throwing an inflated toy balloon. A line is marked on the floor, and the thrower may use any method of throwing as long as he does not step on or over this line. His throw is measured from the line to the spot at which the balloon first touches the floor.

2. BALLOON HAMMER-THROW

An inflated toy balloon has a string about three feet long attached to it. A knot is tied in the string about a foot or less from the end. The contestant grasps the string beyond the knot, whirls the balloon around one or more times, and throws it as far as he can.

3. HANDKERCHIEF THROW

Contestants throw an ordinary handkerchief, or similar piece of cloth, for distance. They should use handkerchiefs supplied by the leader. A player may crumple the handkerchief in his hand, but he may not fold it or tie a knot in it.

4. PLAYING-CARD THROW

Players take turns throwing an ordinary playing card for distance. A difficulty with this contest is that a skillful player can throw the card beyond the length of the room, particularly if the card is perfectly flat. For this reason, an old and slightly crumpled card should be used.

5. SODA-STRAW THROW

Players compete in throwing a soda straw for distance, using any method desired.

6. PAPER-PLATE THROW

Players throw an ordinary paper plate for distance. Like Playing-Card Throw, this contest might develop some throws too long for the room, but this difficulty can be handled and the contest is worth a trial.

7. BALL BLOW

A table-tennis ball is placed on the floor behind a line, and players take turns in blowing it for distance, each player being allowed only one blow. The ball should be placed on a rug, not the bare floor. The ball has a tendency to curve and may even turn back toward the blower, but each blow is measured to the point at which the ball comes to rest.

8. ROCKET SHOOT

Each contestant has a long toy balloon. He blows up the balloon and holds its mouth with his fingers. Then he releases his hold so that the escaping air propels the balloon. The one whose balloon comes to rest farthest from the starting line is the winner. Players may take turns in releasing the balloons, or all may do so at the same time.

9. CORK FLIP

Each player has a small cork marked with his initial. He places the cork on the floor, or on a table, and flips it by snapping a middle finger. The winner, of course, is the one whose cork goes farthest.

Section II: Pin bowling

10. GOLF-TEE BOWLING

Ten spots are marked on a piece of cardboard in the form of a triangle, like the spots on a standard bowling alley. The spots should be about a half-inch apart, but the exact distance should be determined by experiment Ten wooden or plastic golf tees, with points upward, are set up on the spots. A felt pad or some other piece of soft material is placed eight to twelve inches from the pins. Tiddly-wink disks are placed on this pad and snapped as in the game in an effort to knock down the tees. Each player snaps two disks and scores exactly as in the game of Bowling. If regular tiddly-winks are not available, buttons can be used, one button being placed flat on the pad and snapped by pushing down on its edge with another button.

Other methods of striking the golf tees can be improvised. A cork might be snapped with the finger; or a button or coin might be placed on edge and propelled with a spinning motion by a snap of the finger.

11. MARBLE BOWLING

Like the last one, this game uses golf tees as pins. The bowling distance is considerably greater, about five feet, and the pins are somewhat farther apart, the distance depending partly on the size of the marbles. The player "shoots" the marbles in proper "knuckles-down" style, shooting two marbles at each turn and scoring as in the standard game.

12. SWINGBALL BOWLING

Doorway Tenpins

A softball is suspended by a cord from the top of an open doorway, the ball hanging a few inches from the floor. In the doorway, ten pins are set up in the usual formation; the pins can be sections of broom handle or other pieces of wood, but any of a great variety of substitutes will work quite as well provided they are eight to ten inches tall and can be readily upset. Sometimes empty bottles are used. The player takes the ball and carries it any desired distance away from the doorway with the *headpin farthest away from him.* He releases the ball so that it will swing past the pins without hitting them but will hit them on the return swing. He takes two swings on each turn and scores as in the standard game. This game is adaptable to a variety of situations; it can even be played with a large and heavy ball and standard bowling pins. It deserves some experimenting.

13. CANDLE BOWLING

Ten lighted candles are set up, about four inches apart, in tenpin formation on a table. A low pile of books, upon which the "bowler" rests his chin, is placed about eighteen inches in front of them. He blows at the candles in an attempt to put them out, getting two blows at each turn and scoring as in the game of Bowling.

Section III: Ringtoss games and contests

A ringtoss game is one in which players throw small rings or hoops of some sort, trying to make them encircle stakes or pegs. The players score according to their success in doing so. In some similar games, a player can score by coming close to the pin without actually encircling it, as in Horseshoe Pitching. Such games are here classed as Proximity Games and are described in Section IV.

14. RINGTOSS

In this game players throw rings at wooden stakes. The rings are about six inches in diameter and are traditionally made of rope, but other materials, especially sponge rubber, are just as good. There are two stakes, each consisting of a wooden rod about three-fourths of an inch in diameter projecting vertically from a flat wooden base about a foot square; the base sits on the floor, and the pin projects about a foot upward from the floor. The pins are located at any convenient distance. The players have five rings each. They stand at one of the pins and the first player throws all five of his rings; then the other player throws his five at the other pin. Each ring that encircles the pin counts one point for the thrower. The players walk over to the pin at which they have just thrown, count the score and remove the rings, and then throw them at the other pin. The one who gets the larger score in any inning throws first in the next and continues to throw first until his opponent gets a larger score.

It is possible for more than two players to compete, each for himself, but the game is best with either two or four players. If four play, they form two partnerships, and the two members of each pair stand at opposite pins. Then two opposing players throw the rings in one direction, and their partners throw them back, exactly as in Horseshoe Pitching.

The same game is often played under a variety of other names with improvised equipment. Smaller rings are used, usually fruit-jar rubbers. They may be thrown at clothespins stuck onto the edges of boxes, at the legs of upturned chairs, or at glass bottles.

15. THROW-AND-CATCH RINGTOSS

This is a comical version of Ringtoss played by teams of two, one throwing the rings and one holding the pin. One partner sits on the floor and holds a clothespin in his teeth, while the other throws an allotted number of fruit-jar rings at the pin. It is perfectly permissible for the partner who holds the pin to move in an attempt to make a throw successful.

16. THREE-PEG RINGTOSS

The target consists of three pegs of equal height in line with the throw. The peg nearest the thrower counts one, the farthest one two, and the middle one three. The game can be adapted to any kind of Ringtoss equipment, but jar rubbers and nails are usually used. As in the other games, each player throws a prescribed number of rings, and scores are compared. The three pegs should be fairly close together.

17. CHAIR RINGTOSS

A chair is turned upside down and its seat supported on another chair so that the legs project vertically upward. Each player throws four rings, one at each of the chair legs. He scores one point for each success and gets a bonus of three points if he rings all four. For this game to be a success, ringing the legs must be relatively easy, to give a thrower a reasonable chance of ringing all four legs. Accordingly, if jar rubbers are to be used the throwing distance should be quite short, and it is better to use larger rings if possible.

18. QUINCUNX RINGTOSS

The principle of this game is identical with that of Chair Ringtoss. The target consists of five nails, clothespins, or the like, in the form of quincunx, that is, one at each corner of a square and one in the center. The player throws five rings and scores one for each success, with a bonus of three for ringing all five pins.

19. RING TWO

Six bottles are used as pegs. Four of them are at the corners of a square measuring from two to four feet on a side; the other two are side by side in the center of the square. Players throw embroidery hoops or some other kind of rings from a suitable distance, each throwing five in turn. A player scores one point for ringing any one bottle, including one of the pair in the center, but he scores *four* points if he rings both of the center pair with one hoop. There is no point to this game unless the spacing of the bottles and the size of the rings are such that players will sometimes throw at the center pair of bottles and sometimes at the corner ones. It must be relatively easy to ring a corner bottle and score one point, and difficult to ring the center pair, but the reward for the latter must be sufficient to make the attempt attractive.

20. GRADUATED RINGTOSS

This game requires a set of rings that may be difficult to provide, but it is an exceptionally good game and justifies a considerable effort. Each player throws five rings, and these are of five different sizes, say eight, seven, six, five, and four inches in diameter. He throws these in order of size, beginning with the largest, all from the same distance, and all at the same standard peg. He scores one point for ringing the peg with the largest ring, five points for the smallest, and two, three, and four respectively for the others.

21. SCORING RINGTOSS

The target for this game consists of a board with several upright pegs, each with a score assigned to it. There are many possible arrangements of the pegs, but the one shown in the diagram is one of the best. Players throw rings of rope, rubber, wire, or other material. Players throw alternately until each has thrown five, then the rings are retrieved and a new inning begun.

```
5     5     5     5
   10    10    10
      25    25
         50
```

The distance between pegs should be about the same as the diameter of a ring. Conditions must be adjusted to insure that the game is a true diagram-target game; that is, that a player can quite easily ring a pin without actually aiming at it. If the dimensions are not correct, when a player aims for a certain ring there is no likelihood that he will score on any other ring.

22. HOOK-BOARD TOSS

This game is identical in principle with the preceding one. The target is a vertical board with nails for pegs, and the rings are fruit-jar rubbers or other rings of similar size. It is a very effective game.

23. DODO

Dodo is a special form of Hook-Board Toss. The board is two feet square and has twenty-five nails or screw hooks, arranged as shown.

1	2	3	2	1
1	5	10	5	1
1	10	Dodo	10	1
1	5	10	5	1
1	1	1	1	1

Players in turn throw fruit-jar rubbers or similar rings, one at a time, from a distance of about fifteen feet. Each successful throw scores the amount shown for the hook or nail, but there is a severe penalty for ringing the center or "Dodo" hook. One who rings this hook has his score canceled and starts the next throw at zero. The first to reach a hundred wins.

Section IV: Proximity games and contests

A proximity game or contest is one in which players throw, or otherwise propel, objects at a mark, each trying to have his objects come closer to the mark than those of the other players. Such well-known active games as Horseshoe Pitching, Lawn Bowling, and Curling are based on this principle.

24. HIT THE CRACK

The target is a line on the floor, either one drawn for the purpose or a crack that already exists. Any convenient number can play. Each player is given a certain number of pennies, bottle tops, or any other kind of small disk-shaped objects. From a throwing line parallel with the target and eight or more feet away, each player in turn throws just one coin, trying to make it come to rest as near the target line as possible. When all have thrown, the one whose coin is nearest the crack gets all the coins. The game is continued until one player has lost all his coins; then each other player scores one point for each coin in his possession.

In a variation of the game, there are only two players, each taking his turn throwing two coins. The man with the coin closest to the crack scores one point and if he also has the second closest coin he scores two points. This is, of course, the same scoring system as used in Horseshoe Pitching. The score can be kept by transferring coins from one player to another, as in the basic form, if desired.

25. INDOOR LAWN-BOWLING

In this game players roll small balls along the floor, causing them to come to rest as near as possible to another small ball that serves as a target. There is considerable choice in the kind of ball to be rolled: tennis balls could be used but smaller rubber balls are better; marbles are satisfactory, but best of all is the table-tennis ball. The ball that serves as the target (called the *jack* in Lawn Bowling) can also be varied. The jack should be smaller than the bowled balls, but it must be heavy enough to have a certain degree of stability; that is, a bowled ball should move the jack only a short distance when it strikes it. The game is played one against one (singles) or two against two (doubles). In either case, each side bowls four balls, and in doubles all bowl from the same line.

The bowlers stand behind a line that is an appropriate distance from the jack and bowl the balls toward the jack. In singles, the two men bowl alternately, one ball at a time, until the eight balls have been bowled. In doubles, two opposing men bowl alternately as in singles and then when they have bowled two balls each, the other two opponents bowl the remaining four balls in the same way. When all eight balls have been bowled, the ball nearest the jack scores one point, and the side that bowled the winning ball scores an additional point for each of its balls that is nearer the jack than the nearest one of the opponents. This is the same scoring principle as the one used in Horseshoe Pitching, except that it permits scoring up to four points in one inning and of course provides no bonus for anything corresponding to a ringer.

26. INDOOR QUOITS

This game is really Ringtoss played and scored like the standard game of Horseshoes. Any of a variety of rings and of stakes can be used, but six-inch rope or rubber quoits and wooden stakes are probably the best. The game is played as singles or doubles, four rings being used in either case. In singles, two men stand at one stake, and in doubles, two also stand at the other stake, the two who are together always being opponents. One man throws his two rings, then the other throws his. In singles, they walk to the other stake and throw the rings back, whereas in doubles, the other players throw them back. Each man scores one point for each ring that is closer to the stake than the closer one of his opponents; if a scoring ring happens to be a ringer, it counts three points instead of one. As in Horseshoe Pitching, all ringers are equal and two ringers by opponents cancel each other. The game is continued until one side has scored twenty-one points.

27. LINE SLIDE

In this game, players slide flat disks along the floor toward a target line parallel with the starting line, each trying to bring his disks closer to the line than those of the opponent. It is an adaptation of the more formal game, Line Shuffleboard, played on a long table, in which the disks, made of metal and weighing a pound or more each, are propelled by hand. It can be played on a wooden, linoleum, or concrete floor, the disks being slid by hand or by the use of an improvised cue similar to the one used in the standard game of Shuffleboard. The disks should be made of hard wood about six inches in diameter. In singles, each player has four disks. The first one plays his disks and then the second plays his. The second player has the opportunity to knock away the disks of the first, and it is possible for him to do so and leave his own disk in scoring position on the same shot. When all the disks have been played, the winner scores a point for each of his disks that is closer to the line than the best disk of the opponent. A disk that actually touches the line is considered perfect, and all such disks are equal, even though one may barely touch the line while the other is bisected by it. Opposing disks that touch the line cancel each other, and the score is determined by the disks that remain. Sometimes, a disk that touches the line and scores is counted as three points, like a ringer in Horseshoe Pitching.

In doubles, one man plays two disks, then an opponent plays two, the partner of the first player plays two, and finally the last man plays two.

28. TUMBLE LINE-SLIDE

In most respects this game is the same as Line Slide, but it includes a new element that makes it different and fascinating. The equipment is the same as in the other game, except that the line that constitutes the target is the end of a table or other elevated surface, so that a disk that goes beyond the line will fall off and be out of play. The players must try to control the disks so that they do not slide too far. If an elevated surface is not available, the principle can be adapted to a flat surface simply by ruling that a disk that goes beyond the line is out of play and is not to be considered in the scoring.

29. SQUAILS

Crokinole

Squails is an ancient game that is now seldom if ever played under this name. Crokinole is a trade name of a modern form of the game, and is played on one of the commercially manufactured game boards sometimes known as "Crokinole Boards." An ordinary card table is perfect for playing Squails. A large circle must be drawn on the table, its circumference coming within four or five inches of the edge of the table. A spot is marked in the center of the table. Each player has from four to eight disk- or doughnut-shaped objects about an inch in diameter; checkers will serve the purpose. Two players take turns in driving one disk at a time from outside the circle and toward the center, the driving being done by snapping the object with the middle finger. Scoring is based on the position of the objects after all have been played, but several different scoring systems are possible. In one system, only one point is scored during each inning, this one naturally being determined by the one object that is nearest the center spot. In another system, the Horseshoes method of scoring is used; that is, only one man can score, but he can score more than one point if he has more than one object in a position better than the best of his opponent. In still another system, two or three concentric circles are drawn around the center spot, and point values are assigned to the circles.

When the game is played as doubles, it is no different from singles, except that teammates alternate in playing the objects.

Section V: Hit-or-miss contests

This section includes contests in which the player tries to hit a simple target, commonly a receptacle into which he tries to throw objects; he gets credit for a hit and no credit for a miss. There are no degrees of success except that measured by the number of hits.

GROUP A: OBJECTS ARE NOT THROWN

In most hit-or-miss contests, objects are thrown at a target, but in a few they are projected by other methods, such as dropping, striking with a stick, or flicking with the finger.

30. CARD DROP

A small box or pan is placed on the floor behind and close to a straight-backed chair. Each contestant is given ten playing cards. He stands in front of the chair and drops the cards one at a time, trying to get them into the receptacle. He may touch the back of the chair, but must not hold his hand lower than the top of the chair back. He scores one point for each card that drops into the receptacle.

31. CLOTHESPIN DROP

Reaching over a chair as in Card Drop, the contestant tries to drop ten clothespins, one at a time, into a quart milk bottle.

32. BEAN DROP

The contestant is given ten dried beans. He stands erect, holding a bean as high as his chin, and tries to drop the bean into the bottle. He tries ten beans and scores one point for each success.

33. FEED THE FISH

In this contest due regard must be given to the possible damage to floors, furniture, or clothing. If conducted with care, only a slight amount of water will be spilled, and damage can be prevented without too much difficulty. A tumbler or other small vessel is placed inside a large pan filled with water so that it is completely submerged and covered with a half-inch or more of water. Each contestant drops ten pennies and scores one point for each one that goes into the tumbler. The penny is likely to strike the water at what seems the right place, and then skid off to the side and miss the tumbler. The pennies can be dropped over the back of a chair, or from chin height without the chair.

34. TUMBLER PUTT

An ordinary drinking glass is placed on its side on a rug. Using standard golf balls and clubs, contestants take turns in putting a golf ball from a line ten to fifteen feet away. Each one gets ten trials and scores a point for each ball that enters the glass, whether it stays in or not.

35. BEAN SHOOTING

Each contestant has a soda straw and a supply of old-fashioned kitchen matches. Using the straw as a bean-shooter, he tries to shoot matches into a vessel that is placed on the floor about ten feet away. Players shoot in order, each getting ten trials, and score one for each success.

36. TIDDLY-WINKS

Tiddly-winks is a trade name that, like many others, has come into general use. In the game, a player has a number of small disks made of plastic, one disk larger than the others. He sets a small disk down on the table, preferably on some surface not completely rigid; then he presses the larger disk down on the smaller one, and by sliding the large one off the edge of the other causes it to fly into the air. This method of projection can be used in several games, but the most important one, and the one referred to here, is a simple contest in which each player tries to snap a number of the disks into a cup. All players take the same number of shots from the same distance and score one for each disk that goes into the cup.

37. DISK ROLL

The player places a small disk on a table top—it may be a coin, a milk-bottle cap, a poker chip, or anything similar. He holds the disk on edge with one finger on top and starts it rolling, using only one finger. In this way he tries to roll the disk into a small goal two or three feet away. The goal can be made by placing any two straight-sided objects on the table an appropriate distance apart, the distance depending on the nature and size of the disks and on the length of the roll. Each player takes a prescribed number of trials and scores one for each success.

GROUP B: LIGHT OBJECTS ARE THROWN

The term "light objects" refers to objects that are so light in relation to their size that the resistance of the air prevents their being thrown in the normal way.

38. SODA-STRAW THROW FOR ACCURACY

The target is a circle, or near circle, made from a wire coat hanger hung from a support six feet or so high. The players take turns in throwing soda straws from a line a few feet away and score one point for each straw that goes through the target.

39. PLATE PITCH

Players throw objects at a plate. A heavy china or earthenware plate is placed on the floor. The players throw poker chips, milk bottle caps, or the like at the plate and score a point for each one that remains on the plate. The plate, the missiles, and the throwing distance are such that a disk landing on the plate has a good chance of sliding off.

40. PLATE TOSS

In this contest players actually throw plates, that is, paper plates. They throw them at a target made from a coat hanger, the same target but somewhat larger than that used for Soda Straw Throw for Accuracy.

41. SHUTTLE TOSS

Players throw shuttlecocks (those used in Badminton) at the same wire target as used in Plate Toss. The throwing distance must be determined by experiment. As in all similar contests, players take turns, each one taking ten throws and scoring one point for each success.

42. PLAYING-CARD TOSS

The player, holding a number of playing cards, sits on a chair. A few feet in front of him is an upturned hat, a wastebasket, or some similar receptacle. He tosses the cards one at a time, trying to throw them into the receptacle. The number of cards to be thrown can be varied at will, but at least twenty should be used, and a whole deck if time permits. The cards are thrown in rather rapid succession.

43. PAPER-PLATE TOSS

The player throws five or six paper plates, one at a time, in an attempt to make them land in a bushel basket or some similar receptacle. The throwing distance is about ten feet.

Group C: Standard Objects Are Thrown

44. BEAN THROW

Each contestant throws ten dried beans at a hat, small basket, or similar receptacle from a distance of about ten feet, and scores a point for each one that lands in the receptacle. This contest is subject to unlimited variation. Any appropriate small objects, such as peanuts, kernels of corn, buttons, or paper clips, can be substituted for the beans, and any of a great variety of receptacles can be used. The objects must be small but reasonably heavy for their size, and the receptacle should be such that an object thrown in it will not bounce out.

45. BEAN BOTTLE-THROW

Each contestant throws ten dried beans at an upright milk bottle, from a distance of four or five feet, scoring one for each bean that goes into the bottle.

46. BASKET BOUNCE

A basket or other receptacle is placed on the seat of a chair, and players take turns in throwing a tennis ball so that it strikes the floor and bounces into the basket. As a variation, the chair may be turned so that the ball must hurdle the chair's back before reaching the basket.

47. EGG-CARTON BOUNCE

A paper egg carton, the kind with twelve small compartments, is placed on the floor. Players take turns in throwing a table-tennis ball, or other small ball, so that it will strike the floor and bounce into the carton. One point is scored for a ball that remains in any one of the compartments.

48. BEANBAG BOARD

A wooden board about ten inches wide and three feet long has three holes, each of a different size, cut in it. The holes are usually, but need not be, circular. Diameters of four, five and a half, and seven inches are suggested. One end of the board is raised so that the board forms an angle of thirty degrees with the floor, the low end toward the throwing line. Each player in turn throws three beanbags at the board, trying to get them through the holes, and they score three, two, and one for the small, medium, and large holes, respectively. Game is twenty-one points.

A player should choose between trying for a difficult target with a high reward for success, and trying for an easier one with less reward. Accordingly, the holes must be far enough apart to eliminate the likelihood of one's trying for one hole and succeeding on a different one. Also, the conditions must be adjusted on the basis of experiment to insure that the choice referred to does in fact exist. Such adjustment can be made not only in the sizes of the holes, but also in the size of the beanbags, the angle of the board, and the throwing distance.

This is a very old game that has been played with many variations. The principle is always the same but the number, size, and arrangement of the holes can be varied at will.

49. BEANBAG THREE-TWO-ONE

The point of this game is not in the nature of the activity but in the scoring system. It is described here as applied to a beanbag game, but it must be understood that the same system can be applied to any target throw in which several targets are used.

A square board is used, with ten holes arranged in a triangle, like the spots for tenpins. The board is set up at an angle, and players throw beanbags at it in an attempt to get the bags to go through the holes. The conditions should be such that a fairly good player can succeed about half the time. The holes are numbered in order from one to ten. Each player in turn throws a bag at hole number one; if he succeeds he waits for his next turn, but if he fails he throws a second bag at the same hole, and if he fails again he throws a third bag. One who succeeds on the first throw scores three times the number of the hole, on the second throw two times the number, on the third throw one times the number; of course, if he fails three times he scores nothing. After the first hole, all players throw in order at the second hole, then the third, and so on. Since all holes are the same size, there is obviously a large element of luck in this game. Thus it takes just as much skill to hit hole number two on the first throw as to hit number ten, but the former scores six points and the latter thirty.

Section VI: Diagram-target contests and games

A diagram target consists of several areas or sections with different scores, permitting the thrower to have varying degrees of success. The best known target of this kind is the concentric-circle target used in archery and rifle shooting. With this target, the shooter tries to hit the bull's-eye and gets a maximum score if he succeeds; if he misses the bull's-eye he can still score by hitting some other part of the target. Some diagram targets have sections that give negative scores.

GROUP A: THROWING AT A HORIZONTAL TARGET

50. TARGET TOSS

Three or more concentric circles are marked on the floor, or on some other horizontal surface such as a table top, platform, or box. From a line some distance away, players take turns in throwing beanbags or other nonrolling objects, scoring as the objects lie after all have thrown. In this type of contest "on the line is in"; that is, the object scores for the smallest circle that it touches, no matter how slightly, even though nearly all of it is in a larger circle. This is in contrast to some shuffleboard-type games, which will be described later, in which an object on a line counts nothing at all. This game is subject to almost unlimited variation, depending on the kind of missiles available, the throwing distance that can be used, the extent to which the target surface needs protection, and other factors. For this reason it would be pointless to give exact specifications, and general suggestions will be given instead.

The best number of circles is three, but four or five may sometimes be desirable. The scores for three circles should be five, three, and one; for five circles nine, seven, five, three, one. The throwing distance should be as great as is convenient, and this is not often more than twelve feet. Some experimenting should be done with the diameters of the circles, and six, twelve, and eighteen inches is suggested for first consideration. Beanbags are very good as missiles, but they are sometimes unavailable. Rubber heels are preferred by many, and large steel washers are exceptionally good for some situations. The only requirement is that the missiles do not roll (when properly thrown) and that the target and throwing distance be made appropriate to them.

51. MAGIC-SQUARE TOSS

As most people know, a magic square consists of the digits 1 to 9 arranged in three rows of three digits each in such a way that the sum of any horizontal, vertical, or diagonal row is fifteen. For centuries it has been used as a target for various games (see, for

2	9	4
7	5	3
6	1	8

example, Nine-Holes, page 207) and makes a very good target for the type of game now under consideration. The magic-square target is marked out as shown above, and players take turns in throwing at the target and score as the objects lie after all have thrown. There is no reason why a missile that is on a line should not be scored as in Target Toss, but it is usually understood that the rule of standard Shuffleboard will be followed; that is, a missile that touches a line, no matter how slightly, counts for nothing.

52. ARITHMETIC TOSS

A magic-square target is used, but each player makes only two throws in each inning. If a player scores with one object but not the other, his score is simply that of the space in which the object lies. But if he has both objects in scoring position, then his score is determined by multiplying one score by the other. For example, a two and a seven would count fourteen.

53. TOSS SHUFFLEBOARD

Beanbags or other suitable missiles are thrown at a shuffleboard target and scored as in the standard game of Shuffleboard. Suggestions for the target will be found later in this section under Shuffleboard Games (page 210). There are two important features to be noted about any shuffleboard target: first, an object that touches any line counts nothing; second, there is always an area that gives a negative score. Two players throw in turn, one throw each time, until each has thrown four; then the scores are determined.

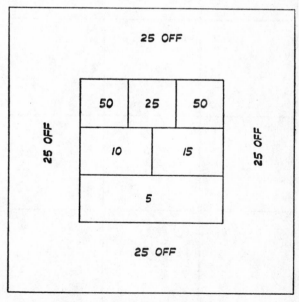

Figure 3. Keep Off the Grass.

54. KEEP OFF THE GRASS

This is a modification of Toss Shuffleboard, in which the negative-score area is greatly extended and hence made more dangerous. As seen in Figure 3, the scoring area is completely surrounded by the penalty- or negative-score area. The rules are the same as for Toss Shuffleboard.

55. BULL-BOARD

As seen in the diagram, the target is a rectangle divided into twelve squares, nine of which constitute a magic square; in the rear row the center square is marked "10," and each of the other two is marked "Bull." The target can be drawn on the floor, but it is better for it to be marked on a board and the rear of the board elevated.

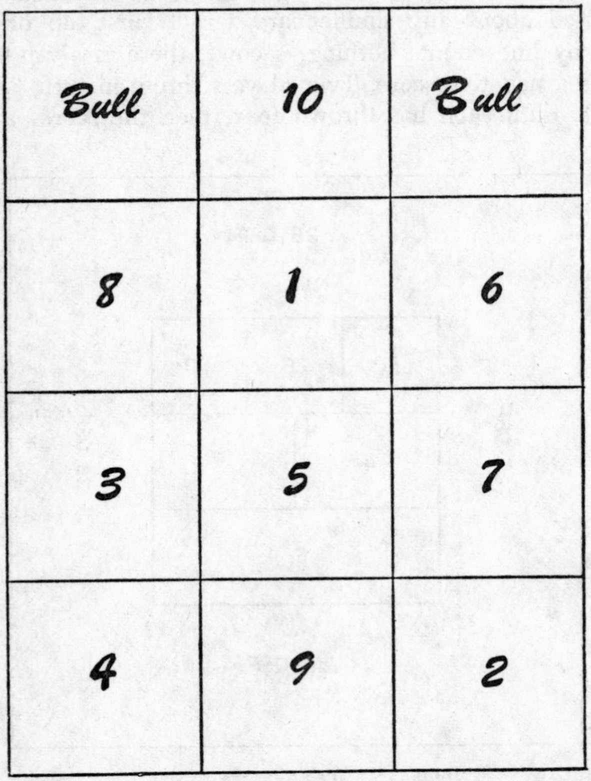

Bull	10	Bull
8	1	6
3	5	7
4	9	2

Figure 4.

A size of three by four feet is often recommended, but a target so large is suitable only when a throwing distance of twenty feet or so can be used. For most situations, eighteen by twenty-four inches is better. Players throw circular disks or other flat objects from any suitable distance up to twenty feet. Four-inch circles cut from linoleum or wall board are very satisfactory; wooden disks covered with felt are probably best of all; rubber heels or other flat objects that do not slide too much are good, too. Although the game can be played easily by three or by two teams of two each, it is essentially a game for two players. Each player has five disks and the two alternate in throwing one at a time.

The distinctive feature of the game is the influence of the bull squares on the scoring. In general, a player's score is the sum of the numbers of the squares in which he has disks after all have been thrown, each disk counting for the highest number that it touches; the shuffleboard rule that a disk on a line counts for nothing is not used in this game. *However,* if a player has a disk touching one of the bull squares, then his score for the inning is zero, *unless* he has disks touching both bull squares; in this case, the two cancel each other and the score is the same as if no bull square had been touched. This regulation leads to several interesting developments in the game. Naturally, a man with one disk on a bull square may try to cancel it with one on the other; he might succeed only to have one of the offending disks dislodged by an opponent's throw, thus putting his score back at zero. He might elect to dislodge his disk himself, instead of canceling it with another.

This game can be played on diagrams of many different sizes. It is sometimes played with a target about one foot wide, with pennies as disks.

56. DOUBLE BULL-BOARD

This game is the same as Bull-Board, except that the target has four bull squares instead of two, with corresponding complications in the scoring. The target has five rows instead of four, a front row that is identical with the rear one being added; thus there is a bull square in each of the four corners, and two "10" squares instead of one. As in the basic game, a player whose disks touch none of the bull squares simply adds his score, but one whose disks touch one or more bull squares has his score affected, as follows: if he touches one bull square his score for the inning is zero; if he touches two bull squares they cancel each other and his score is the same as with no bull squares; if he touches three his score for the inning is doubled; and if he touches all four, his score for the inning is multiplied by four. Game is one hundred points.

57. SEQUENCE BULL-BOARD

This game uses the same target and disks as Bull-Board, but the board should be larger or the throwing distance shorter because of the greater skill required. The object of each player is to score in all of the squares in order and then again in reverse order, that is, "going up" and "going down." Going up, he must score in squares one through ten, then the left bull square and the right bull square; coming down, the order is right bull square, left bull square, then squares ten, nine, eight, and so on down to one.

The players throw in innings of five throws each, as in the basic game. The first player, on his first throw, tries for square number one and, whether he succeeds or not, waits for his next turn. The second player then throws his first disk at square number one. The first player now takes his second throw; if his first disk is in square one he throws the second at square two, if not he throws at one again. They continue thus until each has made five throws; then they start the next inning. On each throw, a player tries for the square next after the one on which he has just scored, but it must not be forgotten that a disk in scoring position can be moved and the score eliminated. Thus, in the first inning a man might hit squares one, two, and three and apparently be ready for four; but if his opponent should dislodge the disk from square two, he would have to start again at two instead of four. On the other hand, if the man scores in squares one, two, and three, and the disks are still in position at the end of the inning, he is safe; credit for these particular squares cannot be taken away from him, and he will start the next inning with number four.

A disk in a bull square out of turn cancels the thrower's score for the current inning, and on the next throw he must start where he was at the beginning of the inning. For example, a man begins an inning with number four and gets four and five and then hits a bull square on his third throw. He is now back to four, but still has two throws in the inning. In general, a disk counts for the square at which the thrower aims, provided any part of it touches the square. However, a disk is considered in a bull square if any part of it touches the bull square.

A slight modification may be an improvement: If, at the end of an inning, a player has disks in a series of squares that are next in order for him, they all count, regardless of the order in which the disks were thrown. This means, for example, that if a player's next square is number five and he gets six instead, he can still score the six if he can throw the five later in the same inning.

GROUP B: THROWING INTO A RECEPTACLE

58. NINE HOLES

Balls are rolled at a target consisting of an inclined plane with holes or depressions in which the balls will come to rest if properly delivered; the score is determined by numbers assigned to the holes. The holes are, of course, always nine in number, but the values assigned to them vary. Sometimes those of the magic square are used, but the ones shown in the diagram are probably better. The balls may vary in size from croquet balls to small marbles, and the target should vary accordingly. The diagram shows a target twelve inches wide, suggested for use with golf balls. The holes are three inches between centers and they must be just too small to allow a ball to drop through. An elevated rim surrounds the board, except at the front. This rim is best when curved as shown, but a square-cornered

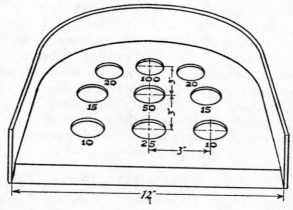

Figure 5.

one is much easier to make and is good enough. The front edge must be bevelled so that the balls will roll easily onto it.

The game is for two players. The first player rolls three balls, and then the other rolls three. The scores are determined by the positions of the balls after all six have been rolled.

59. SEQUENCE NINE-HOLES

The principle of this game is the same as that of Sequence Bull-Board. Since both men cannot score in the same hole, the balls rolled by the first player are removed before the other one rolls. Each man must score the nine holes in numerical order, and then again in reverse order. If in any inning, he scores in the proper sequence of holes, they all count for him regardless of the order in which they were rolled.

60. BOX-TARGET TOSS

A set of three rectangular boxes of different sizes is the target for this game. The middle-sized box is set inside the largest, and the smallest inside the middle-sized one. There must be enough difference in size so that the spaces between boxes will be large enough to receive the balls or other missiles. Beanbags are sometimes used for this type of target, but they are not recommended, because they have a strong tendency to hang on the edges of the boxes; it is better to use balls, which will bounce from the edges. Players throw in order, five throws at each turn, and score according to the spaces in which the balls go—five for the center box, three for the space surrounding it, and one for the outer space. The first to score one hundred, or any other number decided in advance, is the winner.

This game, of course, calls for improvising. The best target of all is one made of concentric circular boxes, but they are usually out of the question; it is more likely to be assembled from whatever boxes can be found. The game is at its best when balls at least as large as tennis balls are used and the throwing distance is fifteen feet or so; however, it works very well with smaller balls or with nonspherical missiles like rubber heels.

61. PAN-TARGET TOSS

In principle, this game is identical with the Box-Target Toss; it is really the same game on a smaller scale. The target is made from any three kitchen vessels, metal or glass. The inner receptacle is a cup or another vessel of about the same size, the middle one a stewpan or the like, and the outer one a large kettle, washbasin, or something of the sort. The difference in size can be quite small. Players throw peanuts (in the shell), clothespins, or other suitable and available objects at this target. The rules are the same as for Box-Target Toss.

62. SKEEBALL

Skeeball is the same as Box-Target Toss, except for the method of delivering the ball. The ball is rolled, not thrown, and the course over which it rolls has an inclined section that causes the ball to jump into the air. The ball must be rolled in such a way that it will roll up the incline and then jump with just the right momentum to fall into the boxes. This game is sometimes played in commercial establishments, where patrons pay a fee for the privilege of playing. In such places the boxes are circular and the balls are wooden ones about the size of croquet balls.

63. MUFFIN-PAN TOSS

Egg-Carton Toss

Players throw pennies, buttons, checkers, washers, or other small objects at a tilted muffin pan. Each compartment of the pan is marked with a number, and the player's score is the total of the numbers of the compartments in which he has coins at the end of the inning. The numbers can be assigned, for example, as shown in the diagram below.

7	0	6
4	10	5
3	1	2
8	0	9

64. MUFFIN-PAN SKEEBALL

This game uses the same target as Muffin-Pan Toss, but the missile is a small ball that is rolled along the floor and jumps from a take-off as in Skeeball.

GROUP C: SHUFFLEBOARD GAMES

The standard game of Shuffleboard requires too much space to be within the scope of this book, but a simplified version of it can well be played at home. Other games that resemble standard Shuffleboard because they are based on sliding objects at a diagram target will be described also. Some of the games included here are to be played on the floor, whereas those on a smaller scale are to be played on a table.

65. REC-ROOM SHUFFLEBOARD

This game is Shuffleboard adapted to the limitations of space in a basement recreation room, and to the equipment available. In Shuffleboard the player slides disks along the floor toward a target by shoving them with a forked stick called a *cue*. In the standard game, the disks are six inches in diameter, but for this game they should be not more than four inches in diameter. Disks cut from wood or other material, or hotdish pads can be used. For cues, it is desirable to have some kind of forked sticks, but lacking these, plain broomsticks will do well enough. The standard diagram is somewhat complicated, and for this reason it is suggested that the one for the game called "Deck Shuffleboard" be used instead. As seen in Figure 6, the diagram consists of the same magic square as used in several games previously described, plus two areas at the ends, one counting plus ten and the other minus ten (usually designated as "ten off"). In the standard game, two of these diagrams are used, one at each end of the court; however, the game is quite satisfactory with only one, the players retrieving the disks after each inning and playing from the same line every time.

Each of the two players has four disks, which must be of different colors or otherwise distinguishable from those of his opponent. From a line as far distant from the diagram as convenient, the players alternate in sliding one disk at a time toward the target. After all

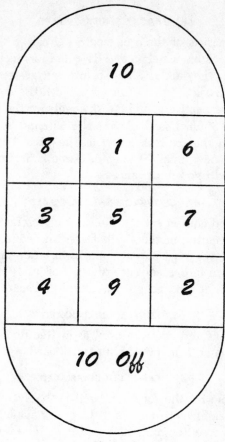

Figure 6.

eight disks have been played, the scores are noted. Here a very distinctive feature of the game applies: Any disk that touches a line, no matter how slightly, is completely disregarded and counts nothing either for or against the player; the only disks considered are those that are entirely within one space or another. It follows from this that the relation between the size of the disk and that of the spaces is quite important, for the larger the disk in relation to the space, the more likely it is to touch a line. It is recommended that the diameter of a disk never be more than half the side of a space.

66. TARGET SHUFFLEBOARD

The target consists of three concentric circles with diameters of something like eight, sixteen, and twenty-four inches. Disks are propelled just as they are in Shuffleboard, but are scored according to the method usually applied to such targets; the circles score five, three, and one respectively, and a disk counts for the best circle that it touches. As in Shuffleboard, players alternate until each has played four disks; then the score is noted as the disks lie, the disks are removed, and a new inning is played. Game is fifty or one hundred points, as agreed upon in advance.

67. SEQUENCE SHUFFLEBOARD

The target and equipment are the same as for Rec-Room Shuffleboard, but the scoring method is that used in Sequence Bull-Board. That is, each player must play the spaces in order, one through ten, then ten-off; then in descending order ten-off and ten through one. If he gets ten-off at the wrong time, he loses all score for the inning.

68. SHUFFLE BULL-BOARD

The same disks and cues are used as in Rec-Room Shuffleboard; otherwise the game is identical with Bull-Board.

69. TABLE SHUFFLEBOARD

This is a game for the fortunate, and probably rare, situation in which a table eight feet or more in length is available. A diagram like the one for Rec-Room Shuffleboard is marked on the table, one at each end if convenient, the squares being about five inches on a side. Disks about two and a half inches in diameter are used, and they are propelled with sticks two or three feet long. That is, the game is identical with the other form, except that it is played on a table top, with a smaller court and smaller equipment.

70. CHECKER SHUFFLEBOARD

A small-scale shuffleboard diagram is laid out, and checkers or similar small disks are shot by snapping them with the middle finger. This is usually thought of as a table game, but it is even better when played on the floor. In this case, the spaces in the diagram should be about five inches square, and the shooting line at least eight feet away.

Section VII: Dart games

The games and contests in this section are all based on throwing darts at a vertical target of some kind. A dart is about six inches long, is nearly always made of wood, and has a sharp point at one end, and feathers, similar to the fletching on an arrow, at the other. The darts are not expensive and can be bought at a game supply store. The board on which the target is mounted presents a few problems. In the first place, it must be considerably larger than the target itself so as to prevent damage from wild shots. In the second place, the board must be sturdy and yet soft; if it is made of even moderately hard wood, the darts will be difficult to remove. The targets for the game have a maximum diameter of thirty inches, or two and a half feet, and it is best to mount them on a board five feet square; if it is not feasible to use so large a board, a backstop should be provided behind the target to catch stray shots. Plain soft wood works quite well, and wood covered with sheet cork or linoleum is widely used; but for most situations, the best board is a sheet of wall board. The target can be marked directly on the board, or it can be marked on paper attached to the board.

In all the games, the darts are thrown from behind a line and must stick in the target. Occasionally, a dart that appears properly thrown will bounce from the target, or stick for a moment and then fall, and it may seem that the throw should be counted; but the rule to follow always is: no stick, no score. Of course, there is some danger involved in these games, and the rule that no one shall ever be in the path of a throw must be strictly enforced.

71. DARTS

This is a simple contest in throwing darts at a concentric-circle target. The number and size of the circles are, of course, subject to unlimited variation. One target in extensive use has ten circles, the largest thirty inches in diameter, and others decreasing by units of three inches; that is, the bull's eye is three inches in diameter, the second circle six inches, and the others nine, twelve, and so on up to thirty inches. A very good compromise is a target with five circles, the diameters being five, ten, fifteen, twenty, and twenty-five inches.

Any number can play, but for obvious reasons the contest is best with two sides of one or two men each. Sometimes the sides alternate in throwing one dart at a time, but it is recommended that they alternate in throwing three; that is, one side throws three, then the other side throws three. The outermost circle counts one, the next two, and so on, so that the bull's eye counts as many points as there are circles. A dart that is on a line counts for the higher scoring circle. In case of doubt, the dart is removed and if the hole made by the dart cuts the line at all, the higher score counts; this is the same rule as used in archery. The winner is the first one to score a prescribed number of points, say 100 or 200, but all must have the same number of throws. That is, with game set at 200, the first thrower in an inning might bring his total to 202, but if the next thrower should score 203 he would win. Sometimes, a special rule is used: To win, a player must score the exact number of points prescribed; if his score exceeds this number he scores nothing for the inning and must wait for his next turn.

72. ARCHERY DARTS

This is not a separate game, but a special form of the game of Darts. It follows, in every way possible, the rules of Archery. Accordingly, the target must have five circles; circles of five, ten, fifteen, twenty, and twenty-five inches are very slightly more than half the size of those on a standard archery target. The circles score 9, 7, 5, 3, and 1. Each player in turn throws three darts, and after all have thrown, and without removing the darts, each throws three more, so that there are six darts on the target for each side. The darts are removed and scored, and a new round or "end" is thrown. It is necessary that the darts thrown by the different players be distinguishable from each other. There is no prescribed number of points for a game, but rather a prescribed number of darts, commonly 36 thrown by each side. The one with the highest score after all darts have been thrown is the winner. The archery idea can well be carried farther by having several throwing lines and a certain number of throws made from each of the several lines, as in the various standard archery "rounds."

73. ENGLISH DARTS

The game of Darts is played a great deal more in Great Britain than in the United States. There the National Darts Association promotes the game and makes the rules. The British target is quite different from the American one, consisting of a circle with spokes that divide it into twenty sections. Each section is numbered, and the scores correspond to these numbers. There is a double bull's eye, one within another, and other complications that will not be specified here. The game is always set at a certain number of hundreds plus one, that is, 101, 201, 501, or even 1001. To win, a player must score the exact number; if he goes over this number he loses his score for the inning and must wait for his next turn. One interesting minor point is that a player's score is always indicated in terms of the number of points that he still has to make for game; for example, if game is 201 and a player has scored 140, his score is recorded as 61.

Because the British target is better adapted than the American one for the development of a variety of games, it is used for many games having different requirements and scoring systems.

74. DART CIRCLE-THROW

The target consists of a single circle, four or more inches in diameter, depending on the throwing distance and the skill of the throwers. Each man is given a certain number of throws with standard darts and scores one point for each dart that sticks in the circle.

75. BALLOON DARTS

An inflated toy balloon hangs in front of a backstop, and players take turns in throwing darts at it. A point is scored when the balloon is broken, no credit being given for a hit that does not break the balloon. The balloon should be small and the throwing distance rather long. The balloons will not be broken so often as one might guess, but even so, a considerable supply of balloons should be on hand.

Chapter 13

ACTIVE STUNTS

ACTIVE STUNTS ARE FEATS OF MUSCULAR DEXTERITY, OR STRENGTH. Most of them require such strenuous exertion, or so much space, as to be beyond the scope of this book, but some of them are quite suitable for indoor use. Such stunts are described in this chapter.

Section 1: Object-manipulation stunts

1. CATCH PENNY

The player raises his right elbow until the forearm is horizontal and the right hand is palm-up beside the right ear. He places a coin on top of his elbow and then, by dropping the elbow suddenly, catches the coin in his right hand. With a single coin the stunt is quite easy, and when it is learned the number of coins should be increased. Several coins can be placed in a row along the top of the forearm, or they can be placed in a pile.

2. FUNNELBALL

A line is marked ten feet or so from a wall. The player stands behind the line, holding a small funnel in one hand and a rubber ball in the other. He throws the ball so that it strikes the floor first, then the wall, and when it rebounds, he tries to catch the ball in the funnel without stepping over the line.

3. NECK THROW

The player stands with his head bent forward and an object resting on the back of his neck. This object might be a beanbag, a well-worn softball, a soft shoe, or anything else that is not too light nor too firm. By suddenly straightening his neck and back, he throws the object into the air and then turns around and catches it in his hands.

4. MIRROR THROW

The player, holding a mirror in his hand, stands with his back to a suspended hoop. Looking only into the mirror, he tries to throw a number of beanbags or other soft objects through the hoop, one at a time.

5. CUT THE CANE

The player holds one end of a cane or wand in his right hand, the other end resting on the floor. He releases the cane, swings the right leg over the top of the cane, and grasps it again with the right hand without allowing the cane to fall. The stunt may be repeated with the left hand or left leg, or with a different direction of the leg swing.

6. SPOON LIFT

An ordinary silver teaspoon is placed on a table, bowl up. The trick is to lift the spoon with one hand, by placing the thumb at the end of the handle and one finger inside the bowl. It seems difficult but, as a little experimenting will prove, it can be done.

7. CARD SNAP

A small card, such as a visiting card, is balanced on the top of one finger, and a coin is placed on top of the card. The trick is to snap the card with the middle finger of the other hand, so that it flies away and leaves the coin balanced on the finger.

8. CANE SNATCH

The player holds the top of a cane with one hand, the other end resting on the floor. He releases the cane, turns entirely around, and grasps it again before it falls.

9. PLATE TWIST

The player balances a plate on the palm of his right hand, the hand being held forward with the forearm horizontal, thumb out, and elbow close to the side. Keeping the plate balanced on his palm, he moves the hand inward to the left and under the armpit. He continues moving the hand in a counterclockwise direction, allow-- ing it to move away from the body and upward, until it has made two complete circles and finishes in its original position. The hand moves in a spiral, counterclockwise and upward and, as has been said, makes two complete revolutions. This stunt can be performed with any object that is not too large, and it is quite effective when done with a vessel of water or with one object balanced on top of another.

10. HOBBLE FEEDING

This ludicrous stunt for two players is sometimes used as a penalty. Two players sit close together on the floor, holding a dish of ice-cream, each player touching the dish with only one hand. Each player also has a teaspoon, but the spoons are tied together by a string so that they cannot be moved more than six or eight inches apart. The players feed each other, alternating in the attempt.

11. DIME ON NOSE

A player lies flat on his back with a dime on his nose and tries to dislodge it entirely by wiggling his nose.

Section II: Coordination stunts

12. CROSSED WIRES

The player grasps his left ear with his right hand and his nose with the left hand. At a command, he must quickly release his hands and grasp his right ear with the left hand and his nose with the right hand. He should be able to shift quickly from one position to the other and back again.

13. PAT AND RUB

This oldtime stunt requires one to rub the top of his head with one hand and simultaneously to pat his chest or abdomen with the other hand. It may be varied by patting the head and rubbing the chest, or by reversing the hands.

14. CROSSED FINGERS

The player extends both arms straight forward, crosses one hand over the other, and interlaces the fingers of the two hands. The palms should be together, the little fingers on top, and the thumbs down. He brings the hands in to his chest and turns them upward.

holding them close to his chin. Now the leader points to any one of the fingers and directs the player to move it. Strange as it may seem, he may find it difficult to do so, and will be very likely to move the wrong finger.

15. RIGHT AND LEFT

The player stands on one foot and swings the other in a horizontal clockwise circle. He extends the right arm downward and after the foot circle has been made a few times, he begins trying to swing his right hand in a circle in a counterclockwise direction. The directions of the circles can just as well be reversed. The stunt is to swing the leg in one direction and the arm in another.

Section III: Balance and strength stunts

16. CAN BALANCE

An ordinary tin can is placed upright on the floor; it is best to use one that has not been opened. A candle in a holder and a box or folder of matches are also on the floor about a foot from the can. The player must stand on one foot on top of the can, the other foot held free of the floor, and pick up the matches, strike a match, and light the candle. He may stoop and bend at will, but must not touch the floor.

17. BOTTLE BALANCE

A quart milk bottle is placed on its side on the floor. The player sits on this bottle with both legs extended straight forward parallel with the bottle. Then he raises one foot from the floor and places it on top of the other, heel to toe, so that he is balanced only on the bottle and one heel. While balancing himself in this position, he must pick up a pencil and a pad and write his name. Instead, he may be required to light a cigarette or a candle, or thread a needle. The same idea is the basis of a contest called Bottle-Balance Race (see Chapter 11).

18. CANDLE BALANCE

This is a stunt for two players. They kneel on the floor facing each other, one holding a lighted candle, and the other an unlighted candle. Each man holds his left foot in his left hand and lifts the foot and leg clear of the floor, so as to balance only on the right foot and leg. This is difficult, but it can be done. While balanced in this way, they must bring the two candles together so as to light one from the other. The same idea is the basis of a contest called Candle-Lighting Race (see Chapter 11).

19. BROOM LEVER

The player stands erect, one hand holding the end of the handle of a broom, the corn end of the broom resting on the floor. Now, holding his arm straight, he must lift the corn end of the broom gradually from the floor until the broom and his arm are horizontal at shoulder height. This stunt requires unusual strength and gives a strong man a chance to demonstrate his ability. The difficulty can be decreased, of course, by using a lighter broom or one with a shorter handle. The stunt is easier, too, if a grasp at a certain marked distance below the end of the handle is permitted.

20. CHAIR LIFT

An ordinary straight-backed chair stands on the floor. The player kneels beside the chair, grasps the bottom of one of the rear legs, and tries to lift the chair from the floor. This is not entirely a matter of strength, and one who fails on the first attempt can probably develop the knack. A more difficult variation is to lift the chair by one of the front legs.

21. CHAIR LEVER

The player stands behind an ordinary straight-backed chair and grasps both sides near the top. Holding his arms straight, he lifts the chair forward until his arms and the back of the chair are parallel with the floor.

Section IV: Wall and chair stunts

22. WALL FOOT-PIVOT

The player stands near a wall and places the sole of one foot flat against it, in any desired position. He now jumps over this foot with the other one without moving the foot from the wall.

23. WALL HEAD-PIVOT

A line is marked on the floor about two feet from a wall. The player leans forward, places his head against the wall, and folds his arms behind his back. Using the head as a pivot, he twists his body in a complete circle, without taking his head from the wall or unfolding his arms.

24. WALL PALM-SPRING

The player stands behind a line that is drawn on the floor some distance from a wall. He leans forward and rests the palms of his hands against the wall; then, by pushing with his hands, he springs back to an erect position. He must not move his feet. This may be conducted as a contest, the object being to spring from the most distant line. Sometimes a player is required to rest only his thumbs against the wall, instead of the palms of his hands.

25. WALL NECK-SPRING

A line parallel with a wall is marked on the floor. The player leans forward, places his head against the wall, and then springs back to an erect stand. The arms are free and may be used to assist in the spring, but they must not touch the wall.

26. PICKUP NECK-SPRING

This stunt is the same as Wall Neck-Spring, except for this addition: A stool or a similar object is placed between the line and the wall. The player places his head against the wall and picks up the stool. He must then spring back to an erect stand while holding the stool. He must lift the stool before starting the spring and must not push against the stool while it is on the floor.

27. TANTALUS

The player stands with his back against a wall, his heels and hips touching the wall, and his knees stiff. A handkerchief is placed on the floor in front of him. He is now told to bend forward at the hips and pick up the handkerchief without bending his knees or moving his heels from the wall.

This is not an honest stunt, because it is impossible for one to pick up the handkerchief in this way (although it can be done if the rules are relaxed to allow bending to the side). The stunt is included because it is very widely known. It is often used as a forfeit.

28. CHAIR PICKUP

The player sits on a straight-backed chair, facing its back, and wraps his legs about the rear legs of the chair. He folds his arms and then bends backward slowly until his head is almost touching the floor; then he picks up a handkerchief or paper with his mouth and returns to his original position. The top of the handkerchief or paper should be a few inches above the floor.

29. CHAIR CREEPER

A small object is placed or fastened on the right edge of the seat of a sturdy straight chair. An ordinary pin is commonly used, but because of the danger of swallowing it, a small square of paper fastened with a pin or thumbtack is suggested as a substitute. The player lies on his right side on the seat of the chair, facing the back and grasping it with his hands. He is now required to crawl around the back of the chair, moving counterclockwise and with head and shoulders leading, until he is able to pick up the object with his teeth. Then he backs up and regains his original position, all without touching the floor. The exact position of the object is important, and shifting it more to the front edge of the chair makes the stunt more difficult.

30. CHAIR CRAWL

This stunt is much like Chair Creeper, except that there is no object to pick up. The player starts from a normal sitting position on a straight chair; he then lies on his right side on the seat of the chair and crawls around to the rear, as before. This time, however, he must continue the crawl until he has gone entirely around the chair and has come back to a sitting position, all without touching the floor.

31. CHAIR BRIDGE

This stunt is quite impressive but not nearly so difficult as it appears. Three straight chairs stand side by side, a foot or so apart. The player lies on his back on the three chairs, resting his head on one end chair and his heels on the other. He now arches his back so that he no longer touches the middle chair; another player removes this chair, leaving him supported only by the end chairs.

The performer may also remove the center chair himself. He grasps the chair, lifts it over his body, and replaces it on the other side.

Chapter 14

STUNT, ALERTNESS, AND CHANCE GAMES

SOME OF THE GAMES IN THIS CHAPTER ARE BASED ON ACTIVE STUNTS of the kind described in Chapter 13. Others are based on the players' active responses to signals or situations. The latter are similar in some respects to some of the games in Chapter 6.

Section I: Stunt games

1. APPLE-PARING CONTEST

Potato Peeling

Each contestant has an apple and a paring knife. The apples and the knives should be as uniform as possible, and if the knives are all dull, so much the better. Each contestant produces the longest possible unbroken strip of peel. The same thing can, of course, be done with some other fruit or vegetable.

2. STORK-STAND CONTEST

A small tin can is placed upright on the floor, and the contestant stands on it with one foot. He remains standing on the can as long as possible; other players may pester, but not touch, him. Each player takes his turn, or several can compete at once, and the one who remains on the can for the longest time wins.

3. BLOW-OUT CONTEST

Each contestant blows at a group of lighted candles, extinguishing as many as possible with one breath. The elimination method can be used in this contest; that is, each in turn blows at a small group of candles, and those who fail are eliminated; then the number of candles is increased and the survivors try again, and again, until only one contestant remains.

4. TAIL ON THE DONKEY

The outline of a large donkey is drawn on a bedsheet or a piece of cardboard and hung at one end of the room. Each player has a paper donkey-tail and a common pin. He stands at the other end of the room and is blindfolded. He is turned around once or twice and then attempts to walk to the donkey and pin the tail in its proper place. The player who places the tail most accurately is the winner.

This game is a very old favorite and is played in a great many forms. Among the combinations that can be used are: whiskers on a cat, horns on a cow, Cupid's arrow on a heart, sail on a ship, cigar in a man's mouth, and beard on Santa Claus.

Section II: Games of alertness or chance

5. THIS IS MY NOSE

All players but one sit in a circle, the odd one standing inside. The odd man goes up to one player after another, points to a part of his own body or clothing and at the same time mentions another. For example, he steps up to a player and says, "This is my nose," but points to his own foot as he does so. When a circle player is thus addressed, he must reverse the process by naming the part to which the odd man has pointed and pointing to the part that he has named. In the example given, the reply of the circle player must be, "This is my foot," and he must point to his nose. This is really quite confusing and someone is bound to give the wrong reply before long. One who does so or one who is too slow in responding trades places with the leader.

6. POUND OR WAVE

This is a simple game based on the same principle as This Is My Nose. A leader approaches those in the circle, one at a time, and in each case he either pounds his fists together, or sticks his thumbs into his ears and waves his open hands. He shifts from one circle player to another quite rapidly, making either of the two motions each time. The circle player must always respond immediately with the other motion; that is, when the leader pounds his fists the circle player waves his open hands, and when the leader waves his hands the other pounds his fists. The first one to make a mistake or hesitate too long trades places with the leader.

7. CORK DICE

The players gather around a table. All players but one have corks or similar small objects tied to the ends of three-foot strings. The corks are placed in a compact group in the center of the table, and the loose ends of the strings are held in the hands of the players. The odd man has a pair of standard dice in one hand and a cardboard box top or similar flat object in the other. The size of this object is not important, provided it can be handled easily; it would be well if it had some kind of improvised handle. The odd man will, on occasion, slam the box top down on the table in an attempt to cover the corks before they can be withdrawn.

The odd man now shakes the two dice and rolls them on the table. According to the system explained in the next paragraph, some combinations of the dice are winners, some are losers, and some are neither winners nor losers. If the roll is neither a winner nor a loser, he simply rolls again; but if it is either a winner or a loser he slams the box top down on the corks, trying to capture them before they can be withdrawn. On a winning roll, each owner of a captured cork loses a point to the roller; on a losing roll, the roller loses a point to the owner of each uncaptured cork. The best way to keep score is by transferring chips or counters, but it can be done satisfactorily with paper and pencil. After a winning roll the same man rolls again, but after a losing roll he loses his turn and the dice go to the next player. The roller may start the box top downward at any time either by accident or by intention, but if he brings it clear down to the table at the wrong time, he pays a chip for each cork that he catches. Likewise, when one of the other players jerks his cork at the wrong time, provided he moves it as much as two inches, he must pay a chip to the roller.

In determining winning and losing rolls, the best plan is to follow strictly the game of Craps (see page 155). If, on the first roll, the sum of the points on the two dice is seven or eleven, the roller wins; if the sum is two, or three, or twelve he loses. If it is any other number (four, five, six, eight, nine, or ten), then this number is called his point, and he continues to roll. In this case he rolls the dice as many times as necessary to get either his point or seven. If he rolls the point he wins, if he rolls seven he loses. When he loses by rolling a seven, he also loses his turn and the dice go to the next man. Other systems could be improvised easily.

8. FIND YOUR PARTNER

To start the game, players are in pairs, forming a double circle facing counterclockwise. One circle faces about, and then the two circles march forward in opposite directions. Suddenly a signal is given, such as by stopping the music to which they are marching, and then each player must join his original partner. In the meantime, the leader, who started without a partner, tries to get one, with the result that one player is left without a partner. The one left out is leader next time.

9. HOW DO YOU LIKE YOUR NEIGHBORS?

All players but one sit in a circle, with the odd man in the center. The odd man goes to any circle player and asks, "How do you like your neighbors?" The reply is, "Oh, not so well," or something of the sort. Then the odd man asks, "Whom would you like better?" and in reply the one addressed names any two players in the circle. These two must immediately try to trade chairs with the undesirable neighbors, that is, the ones at the right and left of the one to whom the questions were directed. The odd man tries to get one of the seats, so that somebody is left out, and this one becomes next odd man. The reply should usually be of the kind indicated, but occasionally it should be a complimentary one, and in this case *all players* must get new seats.

10. VOCAL BLINDMAN'S BUFF

One player is blindfolded and stands in the center of a circle formed by the other players. The circle players hold hands and dance around the blindman, until he gives a signal, and then they all stop in place. To signal he may tap the floor with a wand or cane, clap his hands together, or simply call "Stop." When the circle has halted, the blindman points to one of the players, and the one pointed to must make a vocal sound that has been specified in advance. He may be required to imitate the sound of an animal named by the blindman, or to sing a song. The blindman has one chance to identify the circle player from the sound of his voice. If he succeeds, the two trade places; if not, the same one is blindman again.

This game is not the original Blindman's Buff, in which the blind-man must capture the circle player and then identify him.

11. PASS IT ON

All players sit or stand in a circle. While music is played, they pass some object around the circle, each player being required to take clear possession of it. Suddenly the music stops, and the one holding the object has a point scored against him.

Part Three

PUZZLES AND PROBLEMS

Chapter 15

MATHEMATICAL PUZZLES

Many of the items in this chapter are straightforward problems that might appear in a textbook on high school algebra, and will not be considered puzzles by a mathematician. Some of them, however, will puzzle even the expert, and all of them will puzzle most people.

Section I: Abstract-number puzzles

Group A: Remainder Puzzles

1

A certain number leaves a remainder of one when it is divided by 2, 3, 4, 5, or 6, but leaves no remainder when it is divided by 7. What is the smallest possible value of the number?

2

A certain number, when divided by 2, 3, 4, 5, 6, 7, 8, 9, and 10, leaves remainders of 1, 2, 3, 4, 5, 6, 7, 8, and 9 respectively. What is the smallest possible value of the number?

3

A man had a basket of apples. He gave one of his friends half of the apples plus half an apple. He gave a second friend half of his remaining apples plus half an apple. He gave a third friend half the apples then remaining plus half an apple. He was left with just one apple, which he ate himself. He did not divide any apples. How many apples did he have originally?

4

Five robbers stole a number of coins, all of the same denomination. Since the job of acquiring the coins was completed late at night, and was a rather strenuous one, they deferred the division of the money until morning. Accordingly, they left the coins in some suitable place and all went to bed in different rooms. During the night one of the men became suspicious that the others might try to doublecross him and decided that he would not wait until morning for his share. He tiptoed to the place where the coins had been left and divided them into five equal parts; in order to do so he had to throw one coin away. He took one of the five piles and restored the remainder as nearly as possible to the condition in which he had found them.

A little later a second member of the band got the same idea, and he likewise took what he considered his share. Like the first man, he found that he had to throw one coin away to divide them into five equal piles; he took one of the five piles and replaced the others. Strangely enough, the same thought occurred to the third man, later to the fourth, and finally to the fifth; each of these in turn went to the coins, divided them into five equal piles after throwing one coin away, took one of the piles, and restored the remainder.

Probably each of the five men intended to tell the others that he already had his share, but since doing so seemed to involve certain difficulties, none of them did. They gathered in the morning to divide the money according to their original plan. If the pile seemed unduly small to any of the men nothing was said. They divided the money properly, and it all came out in five equal piles with nothing left over. The question is: How many coins were in the original pile? Or rather, what is the smallest number that could have been in the pile?

This well-known problem has been worked into various stories beside the one told here; for example, the one in which men divide coconuts and throw the odd one to a monkey. Of course, the number of men can be changed, but it is suggested that one who wishes to solve the problem for the first time begin with five men or less. As the problem is sometimes stated, the final division, like the others, leaves a remainder of one coin; there is nothing wrong with the problem in this form, but it must not be confused with the one given.

GROUP B: DIGIT PUZZLES

5

Using each digit once and only once, form two numbers from the digits 1, 2, 3, 4, 5, 6, 7, 8, and 9, so that one number is twice as large as the other.

6

Take the numbers 1 to 10 inclusive and divide them into five pairs so that the sums of the respective pairs are 16, 7, 6, 17, and 9.

7

A number is composed of four digits. The last digit is two times the first; the second is three less than the third; the sum of the first and last digits is twice the third. What is the number?

8

From the digits 1 to 9 inclusive, form three numbers of three digits each, so that the third number is three times as great as the first, and the second number is equal to the third minus the first.

9

Using any desired mathematical symbols, combine six 1's to make them equal 12.

10

Using any desired mathematical symbols, make five 3's equal 31.

11

With simple addition only, make eight 8's equal 1000.

12

Using any desired mathematical symbols, make four 9's equal 100. Make six 9's equal 100.

13

Arrange the digits 1 to 7 inclusive to equal 100.

14

Arrange the ten digits 0 to 9 inclusive to equal 100.

15

Using appropriate symbols, write the digits 9, 8, 7, 6, 5, 4, 3, 2, and 1 so that they equal 100, writing them in the order given.

GROUP C: OTHER ABSTRACT-NUMBER PUZZLES

16

Divide the number 45 into four parts so that adding 2 to the first, substracting 2 from the second, multiplying the third by 2, and dividing the fourth by 2 will all give the same result.

17

If a certain number is reduced by 7 and the remainder multiplied by 7, the result will be the same as if the number were reduced by 5 and the remainder multiplied by 5. What is the number?

18

A certain number is the sum of five smaller numbers and is evenly divisible by each one of the five. What is the smallest possible value for the large number and what are the five small ones that add up to it?

19

A certain number can be divided into two numbers, one of which is twice as large as the other. These two smaller numbers are such that the difference between them is the same as the difference between their squares. What are the numbers?

Section II: Mathematical puzzles on certain subjects

GROUP A: PUZZLES ABOUT AGES

20

An automobile is now half as old as John was when the car was new. John is now fifteen years old. How old is the automobile?

21

A father is four times as old as his son. Twenty years from now the father will be twice as old as the son. How old are father and son today?

22

The ages of a father and his son are the same with the digits reversed. A year ago the father was twice as old as the son. How old are the father and son now?

23

The age of a man plus that of his wife is 91 years. The man is now twice as old as his wife was when he was as old as she is now. What are their ages now?

24

The sum of the ages of a father and his son is 48 years. In a certain number of years the father's age will be twice that of the son, and the father's age then will be eight times that of the son now. How old are father and son now?

25. HOW OLD IS ANN?

The sum of the ages of Mary and Ann is 44 years. Mary is twice as old as Ann was when Mary was half as old as Ann will be when Ann is three times as old as Mary was when Mary was three times as old as Ann. How old is Ann?

This puzzle is without doubt the most famous one in America. It may seem confusing, but a little concentrated thought should lead to its solution.

26

The square root of the year in which a man was born plus the square root of the year in which he died equals his age when he died. The square roots are whole numbers. In what year was he born and in what year did he die?

Group B: Puzzles on Miscellaneous Subjects

27

A brick weighs three-fourths of a brick and three-fourths of a pound. How many pounds does it weigh?

28

Two vessels contain unequal quantities of water, A more than B. A man poured from A into B as much water as B already contained. Second, he poured from B into A as much water as A then contained. Finally, he poured from A into B as much water as B then contained. When all the pouring had been completed, each vessel held 48 quarts of water. How much did each contain at the beginning?

29

A man cashed a check at a bank, but the teller made a mistake, paying in dollars the amount that should have been in cents, and in cents the amount that should have been in dollars. The customer took the money, spent $4.45, and then had left twice the correct amount of the check. What was this amount?

30

A man had 23 coins including dimes, quarters, and half-dollars. He changed the dimes to pennies, the quarters to nickels, and the halves to quarters, and then had 110 coins. How many of each denomination did he start with?

31

A man bought cows for five dollars each, sheep for three dollars each, and rabbits for fifty cents each. He got 100 animals for $100. How many of each kind did he get?

32

Jack had a certain number of dollars and Jill had a larger number. Jill gave Jack as many dollars as Jack had to start with. This seemed a little uneven, so Jack gave back to Jill as many dollars as Jill then had, but Jill insisted on giving to Jack as many dollars as he had at

the time, and this left Jack with sixteen dollars and Jill flat broke.
How many dollars did each have at the start?

Section III: Mathematical puzzles of certain types

GROUP A: CRYPT PUZZLES

33

Each letter represents a certain digit, and only one combination
will work. What is the code?

$$
\begin{array}{r}
S\ E\ N\ D \\
M\ O\ R\ E \\
\hline
M\ O\ N\ E\ Y
\end{array}
$$

34

Replace the x's with the correct numbers to make the division
come out even:

```
x x x )  x x x x x x x x  ( x 7 x x x
          x x x x
          ───────
            x x x
            x x x
            ─────
            x x x x
              x x x
            ───────
              x x x x
              x x x x
              ───────
```

GROUP B: GEOMETRY PUZZLES

35

Assume that the earth is a perfect sphere, 25,000 miles in circumference, and that a metal band fits it exactly at the equator.
The band is cut and an extra piece thirty-six inches long is inserted,
so that the band is now slightly too large. If the band is adjusted
so that it forms a perfect circle and is the same distance from the
earth all the way around, what will this distance be? No allowance
is to be made for expansion or contraction as a result of change in
temperature.

36

A square 200 feet on a side has two circles, each with a diameter of 100 feet, drawn within it. The circles are tangent to each other and to the top side of the square, so that they are both within the upper half of the square. Find the radius of the largest third circle that can be drawn within the square without overlapping either of the two given circles.

37

A ladder rests against a wall, its top projecting above the wall. When the foot of the ladder is nine feet from the wall, eight feet of the ladder projects beyond the top of the wall; when the foot is five feet from the wall, ten feet of the ladder projects. How high is the wall?

38

A, B, and C are three points on a straight line and B is exactly midway between A and C. A fourth point, D, is just as far from A as it is from B, and B is just as far from D as it is from C. If it is ten inches from A to D, how far is it from D to C?

GROUP C: DISTRIBUTION PUZZLES

39

A collection of animals, including both beasts and birds, has 43 heads and 120 feet. How many beasts and how many birds are in the lot?

40

In a certain family that includes both boys and girls, each boy has just as many brothers as sisters, but each girl has twice as many brothers as sisters. How many boys and how many girls are in the family?

41

Jones and Smith, the hunters, shot ducks and rabbits. Jones shot twice as many ducks as rabbits, and Smith shot just as many rabbits as Jones did. All the game together had 21 heads and 54 feet. How many ducks and rabbits did each hunter shoot?

42

Five Arabs had a total of 200 rugs. If the first Arab had had twelve times as many rugs as he actually had, and the second Arab three times as many, and the third the same number, and the fourth half as many, and the fifth one-third as many, the total would still have been 200. How many rugs did each have?

43

In a session of a certain deliberative body, a motion was carried, the "ayes" exceeding the "noes" by 4 per cent of the total vote. If four of the "ayes" had been "noes" instead, the motion would have lost by two votes. What was the actual vote?

GROUP D: RATE PUZZLES

44

A man plans to drive three miles at thirty miles an hour, but for the first mile he is able to travel at only twenty miles an hour. If he travels the second mile at the planned speed of thirty miles an hour, how fast must he drive the third mile in order to arrive at his destination on time?

45

How many minutes per mile do you save by increasing your speed from 12 to 15 miles an hour? From 15 to 20? From 20 to 30? If you are traveling 30 miles an hour, how much must you increase your speed to save one minute per mile? If you are traveling 60 miles an hour?

46

A man drives a certain distance at 60 miles an hour and arrives one hour earlier than if he had traveled at 50 miles an hour. What is the distance?

47

If you drive a certain distance at 40 miles an hour and back at 20 miles an hour, what is your average speed for the round trip?

48

A commuter, going home from work, normally reaches his home station at a certain time and is driven to his house by a chauffeur. On a certain occasion, he arrived at the station an hour earlier than usual, and started to walk home. The chauffeur, leaving the house at the usual time, picked up the man and drove him home, arriving ten minutes earlier than usual. For how many minutes did the man walk?

49

To fill a tank with water from a two-inch pipe requires thirty minutes. How many minutes will be required to fill it with a two-inch pipe and a one-inch one at the same time?

50

A certain pipe will fill a tank in 10 minutes, a second pipe in 20 minutes, and a third pipe in 30 minutes. How many minutes will be required to fill the tank if all three pipes are used at once?

51

If five cats catch five mice in five minutes, how many cats will catch one mouse in one minute?

52

A certain workman is faster than the others, turning out finished products 30 per cent faster; but the quality of his work is lower, so that his products must be sold at 25 per cent less than the others. Should the boss raise his salary or fire him?

53

Two ferryboats start toward each other simultaneously from opposite sides of a river. Each boat travels at a constant speed throughout, and no time is to be allowed for turns. They first meet 700 yards from one shore. Then they pass, continue across the river, turn back, and meet again, this time 340 yards from the other shore. How wide is the river?

Section IV: Mathematical curiosities and stunts

The items in this section are not presented as puzzles, and logically may not belong in this chapter. However, each of them includes an *implied* puzzle—why the numbers behave as they do. For this reason, and because the items are similar to puzzles in other respects, they are included here.

GROUP A: MATHEMATICAL CURIOSITIES

54

Write down any two numbers. Divide one of the numbers by 2 but omit any remainder (for example, if the first number is 117, the division gives 58). Repeat the division by two, always omitting remainders, until you come to the number 1 and can divide no further. These numbers should all be written in what might be called the "division column." Now take the second of the two original numbers and multiply it by two, multiply the resulting product by two and so on, until you have as many numbers in the "multiplication column" as in the other. Now check the numbers in the division column; whenever any of these numbers is an even one (this applies to the first number as well as to the others), cross out the corresponding number *in the multiplication column*. If you add up the remaining numbers in the multiplication column, you will get a number that is the product of the two original numbers.

Example:

Division Column	Multiplication Column
117	51
58	~~102~~
29	204
14	~~408~~
7	816
3	1632
1	3264
	5967

(117 × 51 gives 5967)

55

The number 142857 has some interesting properties. When this number is multiplied by 2, 3, 4, 5, and 6, the products all consist of the same digits as the original number, and in the same order, but starting with a different one in each case. Thus:

$$142857 \times 1 = 142857$$
$$142857 \times 2 = 285714$$
$$142857 \times 3 = 428571$$
$$142857 \times 4 = 571428$$
$$142857 \times 5 = 714285$$
$$142857 \times 6 = 857142$$

If we add one more, multiplying the original number by 7, the result is quite different, 999999.

Derived from these is another set of combinations:

142857×7 is   999 999; divided by nine gives 111 111.
285714×7 is 1 999 998; divided by nine gives 222 222.
428571×7 is 2 999 997; divided by nine gives 333 333.
571428×7 is 3 999 996; divided by nine gives 444 444.
714285×7 is 4 999 995; divided by nine gives 555 555.
857142×7 is 5 999 994; divided by nine gives 666 666.

56

Take the number 12345679 (note that 8 is omitted) and multiply it by any multiple of 9. The product will always consist of a repetition of the same digit, and this digit will be the same as the number of nines in the multiplier, thus:

$$12345679 \times 9 = 111\ 111\ 111$$
$$12345679 \times 18 = 222\ 222\ 222$$
$$12345679 \times 27 = 333\ 333\ 333$$
$$\cdots$$
$$12345679 \times 72 = 888\ 888\ 888$$
$$12345679 \times 81 = 999\ 999\ 999$$

57

Take any three-digit number and multiply it by 11; then multiply the product by 91. The result will always be the original number written twice (for example, $345 \times 11 = 3795$; $3795 \times 91 = 345$, 345). The obvious explanation is that the original number has really been multiplied by 1001, since $11 \times 91 = 1001$.

The same thing can be done with a five-digit number; in this case the original number is multiplied by 11 and the product by 9091.

58

Write down any number of several digits. Under it, write a second number that consists of the same digits in any order whatever, except that the second number must be smaller than the first. If the second number is subtracted from the first, the remainder will always be evenly divisible by 9.

Example:

$$\begin{array}{r} 89645 \\ 56984 \\ \hline 32661 \end{array} \text{ which, divided by 9, gives 3629}$$

59

$$\begin{array}{r} 1 \times 9, + 2 = 11 \\ 12 \times 9, + 3 = 111 \\ 123 \times 9, + 4 = 1111 \\ 1234 \times 9, + 5 = 11111 \\ \cdots \\ 12345678 \times 9, + 9 = 111\ 111\ 111 \end{array}$$

60

Show that 7 goes into 28 thirteen times:

$$\begin{array}{r} 7)\ 28\ (13 \\ 7 \\ \hline 21 \\ 21 \\ \hline \end{array}$$

Prove by multiplication:

$$\begin{array}{r} 13 \\ 7 \\ \hline 21 \\ 7 \\ \hline 28 \end{array}$$

Check by addition:

$$
\begin{array}{r}
13 \\
13 \\
13 \\
13 \\
13 \\
13 \\
13 \\
\hline
21 \\
7 \\
\hline
28
\end{array}
$$

GROUP B: MATHEMATICAL MINDREADING

61

The performer asks a player to write down any five-digit number that does not end in 0 or 1, the number being visible to all. He then announces a number that is to be the sum of the given number and four others, of which he will supply two, all the numbers to be five-digit ones. The player writes a second number under the first, the performer writes one under the second, the player writes the fourth, and the performer the fifth. When all are added, the sum is as predicted.

The method is extremely simple: The number written by the performer consists of digits each of which is obtained by subtracting the corresponding digit of the player's number from 9; thus if the player writes 58276, the performer writes 41723. The total will always be the original number with a 2 prefixed and the final digit reduced by 2; for example, if the original number is 87965 the total will be 287963.

Example:

Original number	67895
Player writes	76543
Performer writes	23456
Player writes	98899
Performer writes	01100
Total, as predicted	267893

62

Ask a person to write any three-digit number, then to write the same number reversed, and to subtract the smaller number from the larger. Then ask him to tell you the final digit of the difference, and you tell him the complete number.

EXPLANATION: The middle digit of the difference is always 9, and the sum of the first and last digits always equals 9. Thus if he tells you 3, you know that the number is 693; if he tells you 7 you know it is 297.

Example:

Selected number	734
Same reversed	437
The difference	297

He tells you 7, and you announce the complete number as 297.

63

Ask a player to tell which of the digits is hardest for him to write. Then ask him to write the number 12345679 (note that 8 is omitted) and to multiply it by a certain number that you give him. The result will be made up entirely of the digit that he has said is hardest for him to write.

EXPLANATION: The original number is always the same, 12345679. The multiplier that you give the player is nine times his selected digit; if he selects 4 the multiplier is 36, if he selects 7 it is 63. The number 12345679 multiplied by 36 gives 444 444 444, and multiplied by 63 gives 777 777 777.

This stunt is an application of the principle of one of the mathematical curiosities described above (Number 57).

64

Tell a player to proceed as in the example:

Write down your age	32
Double it	64
Add 1	65
Multiply by 5	325
Add 5	330
Multiply by 10	3300
Subtract 100	3200
Strike off last 2 digits	32

He tells you the final number and you know his age.

The formula is always the same, and the final number is always the same as the first. The explanation is obvious: the result of the various operations is simply to multiply the original number by 100 and then strike off the last two digits, which are always zeros, to get the original number again. This formula can be varied in innumerable ways. For example, this one multiplies the original number by 10 instead of 100:

Write down any number	57
Multiply by 3	171
Add 1	172
Multiply by 3	516
Add the original number	573
Subtract 3	570

You can stop here, knowing that the last number is ten times the original one, or you can ask the player to drop the last digit (or divide by 10) to get the actual original number.

65

Ask a player to proceed as follows:

Write any number	27
Double it	54
Add an assigned even number (say 14)	68
Divide by 2	34
Subtract the original number	7

After he has completed the subtraction you, without knowing the number he started with, tell him that the remainder is 7. The remainder is always just half the number that you told him to add.

66

Ask a player to proceed as in this example:

Write down your age in years	27
Multiply by 2	54
Add 5	59
Multiply by 50	2950
Subtract the number of days in a year	2585
Add your loose change (under $1)	2638
Add 115	2753

He shows or tells you the final number, and you tell him that he is 27 years old and has 53 cents in his pocket; the first two digits always show the age and the last two the change.

The last step can be omitted and done mentally by the performer. Sometimes the formula is varied slightly by adding 365 and subtracting 615, instead of subtracting 365 and adding 115. Of course, it is not necessary to start with the player's age, and any other number, large or small, can be used instead. For example, you might start with the number of the player's birth month and have him add his age instead of his change; then you can tell him his age and the month of his birth.

67

Ask a player to proceed as in this example:

Write the number of your brothers	2
Multiply by 2	4
Add 3	7
Multiply by 5	35
Add the number of your sisters (4)	39
Multiply by 10	390
Add the number of your grandparents (3)	393
Subtract 150	243

The first digit shows the number of brothers, the second the number of sisters, and the third the number of grandparents.

Section V: Solutions to mathematical puzzles

1. 301
2. 2519
3. 15
4. 3121
5. 13,458 is twice 6,729
6. 6 and 10, 4 and 3, 1 and 5, 8 and 9, 2 and 7
7. 4368
8. 219; 438; and 657
9. $11 + \frac{11}{11} = 12$
10. $3^3 + 3 + \frac{3}{3} = 31$

11. 888
      88
       8
       8
       8
    ────
    1000

12. $99\dfrac{9}{9}$; $99\dfrac{99}{99}$

13.   15
      36
      47
       2
     ────
     100

14. $50\dfrac{1}{2} + 49\dfrac{38}{76} = 100$

15. $98 - 76 + 54 + 3 + 21 = 100$

16. 8, 12, 5, and 20. $8 + 2 = 10$; $12 - 2 = 10$; $5 \times 2 = 10$; $\dfrac{20}{2} = 10$.

17. 12. $(12 - 7)7 = (12 - 5)5 = 35$.

18. 1, 2, 4, 7, and 14 make a total of 28.

19. ⅔ and ⅛

20. 5 years.

21. The father is 40, the son 10.

22. The father is 73, the son 37.

23. The man is 52, his wife 39.

24. The father is 40, the son 8.

25. Ann is 16½ years old.

26. He was born in 1849 and died in 1936 at the age of 87.

27. Three pounds.

28. *A* contained 66 quarts and *B* contained 30 quarts.

29. $15.35.

30. 5 dimes, 8 quarters, and 10 halves.

31. 10 cows, 2 sheep, 88 rabbits.

32. Jack had 6 dollars and Jill had 10.

33.   9567
      1085
    ─────
     10652

34. 1 2 4) 1 2 1 2 8 3 1 6 (9 7 8 0 9
              1 1 1 6
            ──────
                9 6 8
                8 6 8
              ──────
                1 0 0 3
                  9 9 2
                ──────
                  1 1 1 6
                  1 1 1 6

35. 36 inches divided by 2π, or slightly less than six inches.

36. 56.25 feet.

37. The wall is 12 feet high.

38. 17.3 inches.

39. 17 beasts and 26 birds.

40. 4 boys and 3 girls.
41. Jones shot 3 rabbits and 6 ducks, Smith 3 rabbits and 9 ducks.
42. Originally the respective Arabs had 6, 12, 17, 120, and 45 rugs. After the transfers, they had 72, 36, 17, 60 and 15.
43. The vote was 78 for and 72 against; a shift of 4 votes would have made it 74 for and 76 against.
44. 60 miles an hour.
45. Each increase saves one minute per mile. From 30 miles an hour you would have to increase your speed to 60 in order to save a minute per mile. At 60 miles an hour, it is impossible.
46. 300 miles.
47. 26⅔ miles an hour.
48. 55 minutes.
49. 24 minutes.
50. 5$\frac{5}{11}$ minutes.
51. Five cats.
52. Fire him. 75 per cent of 130 per cent is 97.5 per cent.
53. 1760 yards; that is, one mile.

Chapter 16

LOGICAL PUZZLES

A LOGICAL PUZZLE REQUIRES TO A SPECIAL DEGREE THE "FLASH OF insight" that is characteristic of all intellectual problem-solving. The solution is easy provided one gets the point, but the point is likely to be elusive and is often intentionally made more so by the way the puzzle is stated.

Section I: Paradoxes and dilemmas

1. THE HOTEL BILL

Three men shared a hotel room, and each paid ten dollars to the cashier in advance. Later the cashier discovered that the total charge should have been twenty-five dollars instead of thirty, and he gave five dollars to the bellboy with instructions to refund it to the guests. The bellboy in fact refunded only one dollar to each of the three and kept two dollars for himself. Thus each of the men paid nine dollars for the room, a total of twenty-seven dollars. This amount added to the two dollars that the bellboy kept is only twenty-nine dollars. What happened to the other dollar?

2. YOUR MONEY AND MINE

I make this proposition to you: "You take all the money that you have on your person and pile it on the table, and I will do the same. Then whichever of us shows the *smaller* amount will take it all. The odds are in your favor because you have an exactly even chance of winning, and the amount that you have a chance of winning is greater than the one that you have a chance of losing." Is this correct?

3. TOSSING THREE COINS

Is this reasoning sound? When three coins are tossed at the same time, the chances are even that all will be heads or all tails; two of the three will always be the same, either both heads or both tails; and the third coin is just as likely to be heads as tails, and hence just as likely to match the other two as not.

4. THE BEAR HUNTER

A hunter sat down to rest and was startled at being nudged by a bear. The hunter took to his heels and ran straight north for a distance of 200 yards. The bear, being just as frightened as the hunter, also ran, going straight east for a distance of 200 yards. After his run the hunter regained his nerve, aimed his gun straight south, and killed the bear. What color was the bear?

5. THE RAISE

A man who had asked his employer for a raise in salary was told: "Why, you work only eight hours each day, which is just one-third of the day, or 122 days in a year of 366 days. If you deduct 104 days for the Saturdays and Sundays on which you do not work, that leaves only 18 days, and these 18 days are just equal to the four holidays and your two-weeks vacation. This brings the total down to zero, so that in fact you do not work for me at all. Why should I give you a raise?" What is wrong with the employer's statement?

6. THE MARKSMEN

Jim and Bill engaged in a rifle-shooting contest, comparing their success in hitting a small target from a considerable distance. They took fifty shots each and made the same number of hits, twenty-five. After taking time out for a drink, they resumed their shooting. They were not as good this time, for Jim got only three hits in thirty-four shots, while Bill got no hits at all in twenty-five shots. Since Jim's record after the drink was better than Bill's, and since his record before the drink was just as good, Jim's record for the day was clearly better than Bill's. Or was it?

7. THE FIRST CASE

John Lawyer borrowed five hundred dollars from Mr. Jones, his father-in-law, to help finance his legal education, agreeing to repay the loan as soon as he had won his first case. After he secured his degree, John was slow at beginning practice and Mr. Jones sued him for the money. Mr. Jones said, "If I win the suit I will collect the money; if I lose the suit, John will have won his first case and must pay me according to the terms of our agreement, and so I cannot lose." On the other hand John argued, "If I win the suit I will not have to pay, but if I lose the suit I will not have won my first case, and still will not have to pay, according to the agreement." How can these arguments be reconciled?

8. WHO SHAVES THE BARBER?

In a certain community the only barber shaves all the men who do not shave themselves. That is, every man either shaves himself or is shaved by the barber, and no man does both. The question is, who shaves the barber?

Section II: Misdirection puzzles

9. THE ROPE LADDER

A ship tied up in a harbor has a rope ladder hanging over its side. Each rung of the ladder is one inch in diameter and the rungs are eight inches apart, center to center. The ladder hangs down into the water, the water just covering the fifth rung from the bottom. If the tide rises at a uniform rate of twelve inches per hour, how many rungs will be submerged after two hours?

10. THE BUSY BEE

Two automobiles leave simultaneously from points fifty miles apart and travel directly toward each other until they meet. One car travels at a uniform rate of thirty miles per hour, the other at a uniform rate of twenty miles per hour. As the cars start, a bee leaves the radiator ornament of one car and travels directly to the other at a speed of 100 miles per hour. As soon as he reaches the second car, he turns around and flies back to the first, and continues to shuttle from one to the other until the cars meet, always flying at the same speed. How far does the bee fly?

11. THE BOOKWORM

On a library shelf is a three-volume set of books. Each book is two inches thick from the front of the first page to the back of the last page and has covers one-eighth of an inch thick. A worm eats through the paper and covers from the first page through the last page of the set. How far does the worm travel?

12. THE SAILOR AND THE DOUGHNUTS

A customer in a restaurant ordered two cups of coffee and three doughnuts. He dunked one doughnut in one cup of coffee and two doughnuts in the other. The waitress, noticing his actions, said, "What are you doing there, sailor?" How did she know that he was a sailor?

13. THE CIGARETTE BUTTS

A man buys five cigarettes each day. When he smokes a cigarette he saves the butt, and when he has five butts he makes another cigarette from them. If he buys cigarettes for twenty-five days, how many will he be able to smoke?

14. THE WELDED CHAIN

If the charge for cutting a link is fifty cents and for welding a link fifty cents, how much should a man charge for making one long chain from five short chains of three links each?

15. THE TRAPPER'S SHACK

Hank Bent, the old trapper, has been out on his trap line in northern Minnesota with the temperature at fifty below zero. He is delayed by a blizzard and, almost frozen, is barely able to stumble into his shack. The shack is extremely cold, but a fire is laid in the stove, all ready to be lit. Hank looks at the stove, at the oil lamp filled with oil, at a candle in its holder, and then twice at the single match that stands between him and death from freezing. Which shall he light first?

16. THE CANDIDATE

The Constitution of the United States specifies four requirements for becoming President. The candidate must be at least 35 years of age, must have been born in the United States, and must have lived in this country for at least fourteen years. What is the fourth requirement?

17. OUT OF THE WELL

This is a joke puzzle that must be told with the aid of a pencil and paper. The questioner draws a diagram of a well with a man standing on the bottom and another man outside. He states that the man in the well is six feet tall and can reach one foot above his head, and that the man above has a rope that can be made to reach thirty-two feet below the rim of the well. The well is forty feet deep, and it seems that the man in the well can come only within one foot of reaching the rope. "Now," says the questioner, "how can we get the man out?" When all give up, he says, "Why we will *rub* him out," erasing the picture of the man as he does so.

Section III: Miscellaneous logical puzzles

18. GASOLINE AND ALCOHOL

One tank is half full of gasoline and another is half full of alcohol. A spoonful of gasoline is taken from the first tank and thoroughly mixed with the alcohol in the second tank. Then a spoonful of the mixture is taken from the second tank and mixed with the gasoline in the first tank. Now, how does the amount of gasoline missing from the first tank compare with the amount of alcohol missing from the second?

19. THE THREE CANS

You have an eight-gallon can full of water and two empty cans, with capacities of five and three gallons, respectively. How can you get exactly four gallons of the water into the five-gallon can?

20. THE BRILLIANT ASSISTANT

A wealthy man wished to hire a brilliant assistant and had narrowed his candidates to three men, who were assembled around a table in his office. The employer said, "I will blindfold all of you and

I will make one mark on the forehead of each of you, either with a white crayon or with a black one. Then I will remove the blindfolds and whoever of you is able to see one or more black marks on the foreheads of the others will so indicate by tapping continuously on the table. The man who is first able to tell which kind of mark is on his own forehead will rise and explain, and if his explanation is valid he will be hired." The employer then blindfolded the three men and in fact made a black mark on each of their foreheads. In accordance with instructions, all began to tap, but soon one of them rose, announced that his own mark was black, and explained how he deduced this fact. How did he know?

21. THE FIVE HATS

Three men face each other around a table. They are shown a box that all know contains five hats—two black hats and three white ones. They are all blindfolded, one of the five hats is placed on the head of each, and then the blindfolds are removed from two of the men but not from the third. The first of the men without blindfolds is asked to tell the color of his hat, but he is unable to do so; the second man, likewise is unable to tell the color of his hat. But the third man, the one with the blindfold, is able to announce the color of his hat. How does he know?

22. THE COUNTERFEIT COIN

You are given twelve apparently identical coins, but know that a counterfeit one, with a weight different from that of the others, is included. You do not know whether the bad coin is lighter or heavier than the others, only that its weight is different. You are also given an ordinary equipoise balance, but you have no weights other than the coins. You are to use the balance to locate the bad coin and tell whether it is heavy or light, but you are permitted to use the balance only three times.

23. FOX, GOOSE, AND CORN

A man has a fox, a goose, and a sack of corn, and he must take these from one side of a river to the other. His only conveyance is a boat in which he can take himself and any one of the three. If left unguarded the fox will eat the goose, or the goose will eat the corn. How does the man get them all across the river without mis-hap?

24. MISSIONARIES AND CANNIBALS

Three missionaries and three cannibals are traveling together and come to a river that they must cross in a boat that will hold only two men. The cannibals seem friendly enough but the missionaries are cautious. How can they arrange to get all six across the river without ever having the missionaries outnumbered by the cannibals on either side?

25. THREE PLAYING CARDS

There are three playing cards in a row. A diamond is on the left of a spade (not necessarily next to it); an eight is on the right of a King; a ten is on the left of a heart; a heart is on the left of a spade. What are the three cards?

26. THE LAST MISSION

During the Korean Conflict an American aviator was flying his last mission before his scheduled discharge. He was thinking of his trip home and of the many things that he would do when he got there. Suddenly an enemy plane shot him down and when discovered he was dead. What is wrong with this story?

27. COVER THE TABLE

Each of two men has an unlimited supply of coins, all of the same size. They play a game in which they alternately place one coin at any desired spot on the top of a small table, the winner to be the one who places the last coin, leaving insufficient room for his opponent to add one. It is possible for the one who plays first to be sure of winning. How can he do this?

28. THE FLOATING HAT

A man is rowing a boat in a river that flows in a straight line and with a perfectly uniform velocity. There is a marker at each mile on the bank of the river. He rows upstream past the first mile marker and then past the second. As he is even with the second marker, his hat blows off and floats on the water. He continues upstream for ten minutes after losing his hat, and then turns around and rows downstream. When he reaches the first mile marker he overtakes his hat. What is the speed of the current in the river?

29. A FOR WHAT?

There is something fishy about the following telephone conversation. What is it?

"Good morning. Boone County Merchandising Company."

"May I talk with Mr. Callahan, please?"

"Who is calling, please?"

"This is George Edwards."

"Beg pardon, I didn't catch the name." .

"George Edwards; *E* for evangelical, *D* for diversification, *W* for waterproof, *A* for antagonistic . . . ."

"Excuse me, sir, but *A* for what?"

"*A* for antagonistic, *R* for reprehensible, *D* for developmental, *S* for sacroiliac, Edwards."

"Thank you, sir, Mr. Callahan is ready to talk."

30. BLACKFEET AND WHITEFEET

A Whitefoot always tells the truth and a Blackfoot always lies. A stranger approached a group of three men, each known to belong to one or the other of these tribes, and asked one of them, "Are you a Whitefoot or a Blackfoot?" The man addressed answered the question, but his answer was not understood by the questioner. The second of the three said, "His answer was that he is a Whitefoot, and he tells the truth." The third one of the group added, "The second man, who just spoke, is a Blackfoot." To which of the tribes does each of the three belong?

Section IV: Solutions to logical puzzles

1. The question is a fraud, for there is no point in adding 27 and 2, and hence there is no "other dollar." The proper question is, "What happened to the thirty dollars?" and the answer is that the clerk got twenty-five, the bellboy got two, and the guests had three dollars returned to them. .

2. The reasoning is obviously incorrect, for it applies equally well to both men, and both cannot have an advantage. If you know how much money you have and can guess how much I have, then the problem is one of shrewdness, not of chance. The problem is stated as one in probabilities, and for it to be such, the amounts held by the two of us must be determined by chance. In this case, it is true that you are just as likely to

win as to lose, but it is also true that the amount that you might win
and the amount that you might lose are identical.

3. The reasoning is faulty; there is only one chance in four that all three
   coins will be alike. The reasoning would be correct only if we could
   toss two coins and be sure that they would be alike.

4. The conditions of the problem are possible at the North Pole. Probably
   no bears are there, but if there were any they would be Polar Bears and
   hence white. This is not, as is commonly believed, the only solution. If
   the man and bear collided within a few yards of the *South* Pole, the
   bear could travel 200 yards east and return to his starting point by
   going entirely around the earth. If he started even nearer to the pole,
   he would travel around the earth two, three, or any number of times.

5. This is intended more as a joke than as a serious problem. Of course, the
   point is that the employer should have deducted only one-third of the
   Saturday, Sunday, and holiday time. If he had done this, he would have
   found that the man actually worked the equivalent of 81⅓ days of 24
   hours each.

6. No, Jim's record was not better than Bill's but just equal to it. The only
   proper way to measure the marksmanship is by the ratio of hits to attempts. Jim's rating was 28/84 and Bill's was 25/75, so that they tied
   with a rating of .333.

7. This puzzle, like number 8, has no solution, because the statement is self-
   contradictory.

8. This problem, like number 7, has no solution, because the statement is
   self-contradictory.

9. The number of submerged rungs will not change, because the boat will
   rise with the tide.

10. Since the cars start 50 miles apart and approach each other at 50 miles
    per hour, they must meet in exactly one hour; since the bee flies for one
    hour at the rate of 100 miles per hour, he will fly 100 miles.

11. The worm will eat through only the cover of volume one, all of volume
    two, and only the cover of volume three, a total distance of two and a
    half inches.

12. The customer was wearing a sailor suit.

13. In twenty-five days the man will buy 125 cigarettes; from the butts of
    these he will make 25 other cigarettes, from the butts of the 25 he will
    make five, and from the butts of the five he will make one, so that he will
    have altogether 156 cigarettes.

14. $3.00. He will cut the three links of one of the pieces and use them to
    join the other pieces.

15. He will first light the match.

16. The fourth requirement is that he be elected.

17. No solution required.

18. No computation is needed to see that the two amounts must be the same.

19. Fill the 5-gallon can. Fill the 3-gallon can from the 5-gallon can, leaving
    2 gallons. Empty the 3-gallon can into the 8-gallon can, and transfer
    the 2 gallons from the 5-gallon to the 3-gallon can. Fill the 5-gallon can
    from the 8-gallon can. Fill the 3-gallon can from the 5-gallon can, leaving
    4 gallons in the 5-gallon can.

20. *A* reasons: "My mark is black because the things that would happen if
    it were white are not in fact happening. If my mark were white, then *B*
    (or *C* just as well) would know that his is black, for otherwise *C* would

have no reason for tapping. Since *B* has not inferred that his mark is black, I infer that this situation (the one in which my mark is white) does not exist.

21. The key to the solution of this problem is that if one of the men sees two black hats he knows his own to be white, since only two black ones are available. The reasoning is essentially the same as in The Brilliant Assistant, but involves an additional step. In brief, the blind man knows that his hat is white because: (a) if it were one of two black hats the third man would immediately know that his own is white; (b) if it were the only black hat, either of the other two could deduce that his hat is white, because the remaining man did not deduce that his hat is white.

22. Place coins 1-2-3-4 on the left pan, and coins 5-6-7-8 on the right pan, leaving the other four off. If the pans balance the problem is relatively simple and will be considered later; assume now that the pans do not balance and that the left pan is low. You now know that the bad coin is one of eight. You do not know whether it is heavy or light, but you do have this important information: You know that if the bad coin is on the left pan it is heavy, and that if it is on the right pan it is light. That is, each of the eight coins can be marked *H* or *L*, meaning that *if it is the bad one* it is heavy or light as the case may be.

For the second weighing, place coins 1-2-5 on the left pan and coins 3-4-6 on the right, taking 7 and 8 off: Note that 3-4-5 have been shifted from one pan to the other, and that 1-2-6 have not been shifted. Again assume that the pans do not balance, deferring consideration of the situation in which they do balance. If the left pan is still low you know that the bad coin is still on the balance, and *that it has not been shifted;* if the right pan is now low you know that the bad coin *has been shifted.* In the former case it must be 1, 2, or 6; in the latter it must be 3, 4, or 5. In either case you proceed with the third weighing as follows:

Lay one of the three coins aside and place the other two on the balance, seeing to it that one of the two is on the same pan as before and that the other is shifted. Then (a) if the pans balance, the bad coin is the discarded one; (b) if the same pan is low as before, the bad coin is the one that has not been shifted; (c) if the other pan is low, the bad coin is the one that has been shifted. Thus you identify the bad coin and you already know whether it is heavy or light.

If on the first weighing the pans balance, you know that the bad coin is 9, 10, 11, or 12. You set 12 aside, and place 9 and 10 on one pan and 11 on the other, adding one of the other coins to equalize the numbers. If the pans now balance you know that the bad coin is number 12, and you have only to compare it with a normal coin to tell whether it is heavy or light. If the pans do not balance you have three questionable coins, and you make the third weighing as described above. You proceed in the same way if the pans do not balance on the first weighing but do balance on the second.

23. He takes the goose across the river, comes back and takes the fox over but takes the goose back to the starting point; on the second trip he takes the corn; then he returns and takes the goose on the third trip.

24. Two cannibals cross the river and one remains on the far side but the other returns. Again two cannibals cross the river and one returns. Then two missionaries cross the river and one missionary and one cannibal

come back. Then two missionaries cross and one cannibal makes two trips back to bring over the other two cannibals one at a time.

25. Ten of diamonds, king of hearts, eight of spades.

26. No one could have known what the flyer was thinking.

27. The first player places a coin in the exact center of the table. Thereafter, wherever the second man places a coin the first man places his diametrically opposite at the same distance from the center. Thus if the second man can play, the first man must be able to do so also.

28. Three miles per hour. This problem involves the principle of relative motion. Since the river is flowing at a uniform rate and in a straight line, any object in the water will move in *relation to the water* in precisely the same way no matter what the speed or direction of the water may be. Consequently, when the man rows upstream after losing his hat, he leaves a certain point on the water, this point being marked by his hat. Since he rows away from this point for ten minutes and then rows back to it, he must require ten minutes to get back. By the time he gets back to the point *on the water* that is marked by his hat, this point has moved, *in relation to the shore,* a distance of one mile. This means that the hat, and therefore the water, has moved one mile in twenty minutes, or at the rate of three miles per hour.

One who has difficulty in comprehending this explanation will do well to consider the following, which is, in principle, exactly the same problem: A man is standing near the bow of a large ship that is moving forward. He walks toward the stern of the ship for ten minutes, then turns around and walks back to the point from which he started. When he gets back to his starting point, this point is one mile down the shore from the place at which it was when he started to walk. How fast is the ship moving? *Answer:* Three miles per hour.

29. The point is that the question "A for what?" would not be asked, since the listener already knows that the letter in question is *A*.

30. The first speaker must have said "I am a Whitefoot," because if he really was one he must have told the truth, but if he was not a Whitefoot he must have lied. The second speaker must actually have been a Whitefoot because he quoted the first one correctly, and since he said the first one was a Whitefoot this also must be the truth. The third man, then, must have lied when he called the second a Blackfoot. Therefore the first and second men were Whitefeet and the third a Blackfoot.

Chapter 17

POSITION AND FIGURE PUZZLES

THE PUZZLES IN THIS CHAPTER ARE CONCERNED WITH LINES, GEOMETric figures, and patterns formed by objects. Included here are puzzles based on the manipulation of figures formed by matches. Puzzles involving solid objects are related to the ones described here, but are necessarily excluded.

Section 1: Line puzzles

1

Place eight checkers on a checkerboard, using both black and white squares, so that no two checkers are in the same line, horizontal, vertical, or diagonal. There are several ways of doing this and it is possible to have on the same board and at the same time as many as four sets of checkers, each set satisfying the requirements. Of course, a real checkerboard is not needed; a diagram can be marked on paper and any counters used.

2

Arrange ten checkers or other counters so as to form five lines of four counters each.

3

Arrange twelve counters so as to form six rows of four counters each.

4

What is the smallest number of queens that can be placed on a chessboard so as to command or occupy all squares?

5

Draw Figure 7 in one continuous line, without crossing a line, retracing a line, or lifting your pencil from the paper.

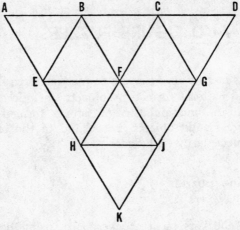

Figure 7.

6

Here is another unicursal puzzle. Figure 8 is to be drawn in one continuous line, without lifting the pencil from the paper, crossing a line, or retracing a line.

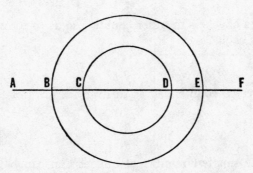

Figure 8.

7

Try drawing the open envelope shown in Figure 9 in one line, without crossing or retracing a line, or lifting the pencil.

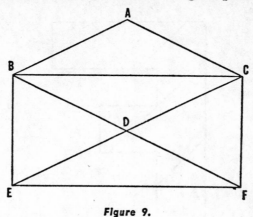

Figure 9.

Section II: Figure puzzles

GROUP A: DISSECTION PUZZLES

8

Divide Figure 10 into four parts of equal size and shape.

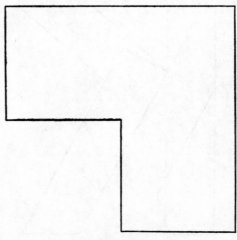

Figure 10.

9

Draw the letter *F* on cardboard and cut it into pieces as show
in Figure 11. Then shuffle the pieces and put them together agai
to form the *F*.

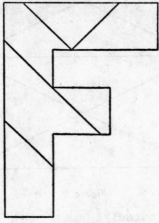

Figure 11.

. 10

Draw the letter *K* on cardboard and cut it into pieces as show
in Figure 12. Then shuffle the pieces and put them back together.

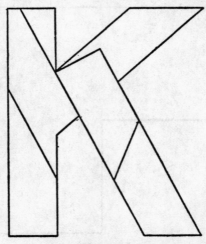

Figure 12.

11

Draw a *T* on cardboard and cut it into four simple pieces as shown in Figure 13. Then shuffle the pieces and see how long is required to rearrange them to form the *T*.

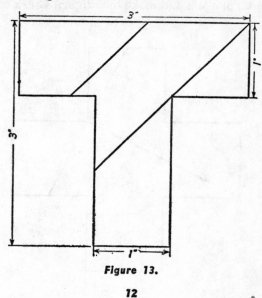

Figure 13.

12

Cut a cardboard *T* into pieces as shown in Figure 14. Shuffle the pieces and rearrange them to form a square.

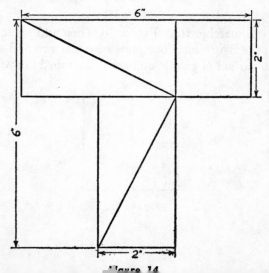

Figure 14.

13

Draw a Greek cross on cardboard and cut it into pieces as shown in Figure 15. Shuffle the pieces and rearrange them to form a square. Then shuffle them again and make the original Greek cross.

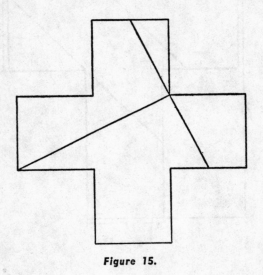

Figure 15.

GROUP B: MATCH PUZZLES

14

With sixteen matches form Figure 16. Then add eight matches so as to divide the figure into four parts of equal size and shape. Note that this is a variant of puzzle number 8 described above.

Figure 16.

15

Arrange twenty-four matches as shown in Figure 17. Remove eight matches and leave only two squares.

Figure 17.

16

Arrange twenty-four matches as shown in Figure 17. Take away eight matches and leave two large squares and one smaller one.

17

Arrange twenty-four matches shown in Figure 17. Remove four matches and leave five squares. ،

18

Arrange twelve matches as shown in Figure 18. Remove three matches and shift two, so as to form three squares.

Figure 18.

19

Arrange twelve matches as shown in Figure 18. Shift three of the matches and leave only three squares.

20

Start with Figure 18. This time shift *four* matches and leave three squares.

21

Arrange sixteen matches as shown in Figure 19. Shift two matches and leave only four squares.

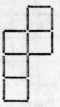

Figure 19.

22

Arrange sixteen matches as shown in Figure 20. Shift three matches and leave four squares.

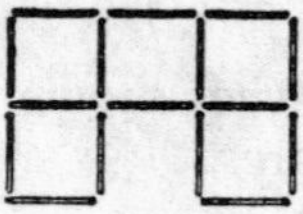

Figure 20.

23

With seven matches form the obviously incorrect equation shown in Figure 21. Now shift just one match and make the equation correct.

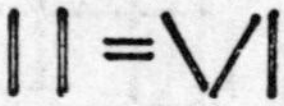

$$||=\vee|$$

Figure 21.

24

With eight matches, prove that half of seven is twelve.

25

Form a row of six matches as shown in Figure 22. Now add five matches and make nine.

Figure 22.

26

Form a row of seven matches as shown in Figure 23. Remove one match and shift two so as to leave nothing.

Figure 23.

27

With sixteen matches make a row of four squares as shown in Figure 24. Eliminate four matches and then shift three and get what matches are made of.

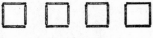

Figure 24.

Section III: Move puzzles

28

Place five coins, three nickels and two dimes, in a row, each coin touching the next ones, with the nickels and dimes alternating. Thus, if the nickels are designated *A*, *B*, and *C*, and the dimes as *a* and *b*, the arrangement will be: *A a B b C*. Make three moves, shifting two touching coins on each move, and leave the coins so that the three nickels will be at one end of the line and the two dimes at the other.

29

Arrange three nickels and three dimes in a single straight line, each coin touching the next ones, the first three coins being nickels and the other three dimes. If nickels are *A*, *B*, and *C*, and the dimes *a*, *b*, and *c*, the order will be: *ABCabc*. Now shift two touching coins at a time, as in the last puzzle, and in three shifts rearrange the coins so that the nickels and dimes alternate and there are no gaps in the line.

30

Place three nickels and three dimes in a row, with a blank space in the middle. The arrangement, with capitals indicating nickels and lower-case letters dimes, is this:

$$A \ B \ C \ (\ ) \ a \ b \ c$$

The problem is to shift the arrangement to this:

$$a \ b \ c \ (\ ) \ A \ B \ C$$

The nickels move only to the right, and the dimes only to the left. A coin may move to the next square if it is vacant, and may jump over a coin of different denomination if the next square beyond that is vacant.

31

This puzzle is the same as the preceding one, except that it uses four nickels and four dimes. The solution principle is the same but the process is longer.

32

Start with ten checkers in a straight line. Take any checker and move it in either direction so that it jumps over two other checkers and is placed on top of the third one. Make a series of such moves and end with the checkers all two deep.

33

Arrange ten checkers like bowling pins, thus:

```
        o
      o   o
    o   o   o
  o   o   o   o
```

Shift just three checkers and reverse the figure so that the apex is at the bottom.

Section IV: Visualization puzzles

34

Which of the two dotted lines in Figure 25 is longer?

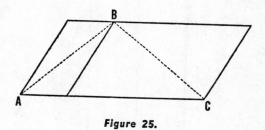

Figure 25.

35

How do the horizontal and vertical line in Figure 26 compare in length?

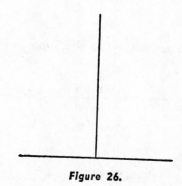

Figure 26.

36

How do the three straight lines in Figure 27 compare in length?

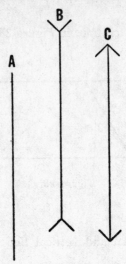

Figure 27.

37

How does the distance *AB* in Figure 28 compare with *BC*?

Figure 28.

38

How many turns will the wheel in Figure 29 make in rolling from *A* to *B*?

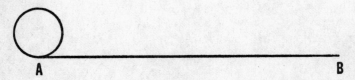

Figure 29.

39

Place three pennies in a line as shown in Figure 30. Then place a fourth penny in a line at right angles to the first line so that the distance *CD* equals *AB*. How do the distances compare in the figure?

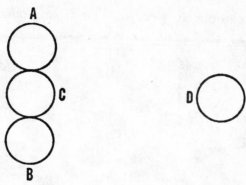

Figure 30.

40

How does the distance *AB* in Figure 31 compare with *BC*?

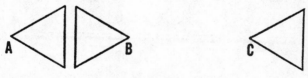

Figure 31.

41

Imagine that you have a single sheet of paper and that you fold it in the middle. Imagine that you fold it again in the middle but in a direction at right angles to the first fold. You now have four thicknesses of paper. Imagine that you cut through the four thicknesses right down the middle of the paper, the cut being parallel with the first fold. How many pieces of paper will you have? How many pieces if the cut is parallel with the second fold?

42

A four-inch cube of solid white material is painted black on all six faces and then cut into one-inch cubes. Some of the cubes will have three black faces, some two, some one, and some none. How many will there be of each?

Section V: Solutions to position and figure puzzles

1.

2.

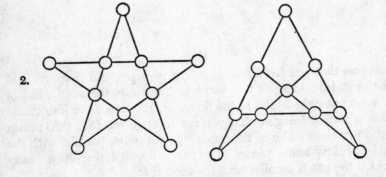

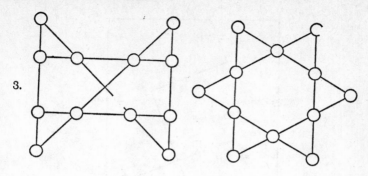

3.

4. Five queens.
5. Start with *C* and take the following route: *C-D-J-F-H-J-K-E-F-B-E-A-C-F*.
6. Take the following route: *A* to *B*; by upper curve to *E*; to *D*; by upper curve to *C*; straight line to *D*; by lower curve to *C*; straight line to *B*; by lower curve to *E*; to *F*.
7. Take the following route: *E-B-D-C-B-A-C-F-D-E-F*.

8.

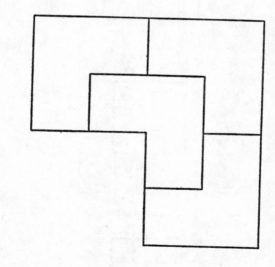

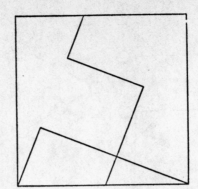

13.

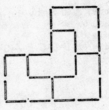

14.

15.

16.

17.

18.

19.

20.

21.

22.

23. $I = \sqrt{I}$ i.e. the square root of 1

24. Half of $XII = VII$

25. NINE

26. NIL

27. LOVE

28. Shift *Bb* to the right of *C*; Shift *CB* to the vacant space; Shift *Aa* to the vacant space, leaving: *C B A a b*.

29. Move *AB* to the right of *c*; Move *cA* to the right of *B*; Move *Ca* to the right of *b*, leaving: *b C a B c A*.

30. Number the spaces left to right: 1,2,3,4,5,6,7, number 4 being vacant. Move *C* to the vacant space and then move so that the spaces are vacant in this order: 5, 6, 4, 2, 1, 3, 5, 7, 6, 4, 2, 3, 5, 4. This makes fifteen moves altogether.

31. Number the spaces left to right, number 5 being vacant. Move the dime from 6 to 5, leaving 6 vacant. Then move so as to leave spaces vacant in this order: 4, 3, 5, 7, 8, 6, 4, 2, 1, 3, 5, 7, 9, 8, 6, 4, 2, 3, 5, 7, 6, 4, 5.

32. Number the checkers left to right. There are several ways of solving the problem; one way is this: 5 on 2, 7 on 10, 3 on 8, 1 on 4, 9 on 6.

33. Move the top checker below the bottom row; then move the two end checkers from the bottom row to the ends of the row of 2, thus making it a row of 4.

34. The two lines are of the same length.
35. The horizontal line is longer.
36. Line *C* is longest.
37. *AB* and *BC* are the same.
38. Two turns.
39. *AB* and *CD* are equal.
40. *AB* and *BC* are equal.
41. Three pieces of paper in each case.
42. Eight cubes with three black faces each; twenty-four with two black faces; twenty-four with one; eight with none.

Chapter 18

WORD PUZZLES

IN THE PUZZLES OF THIS CHAPTER THE PROBLEM IS TO SUPPLY WORDS or sentences that conform to given specifications, or that are translations or interpretations of given material. The best-known ones are rebuses and anagram puzzles, but other varieties are also included.

Section I: Crypt puzzles

GROUP A: REBUSES

The word "rebus" is derived from the Latin, in which language it is the ablative plural of *res*, a thing; *res* is the word that is used in various legal phrases. Just how an ablative plural in Latin developed into a nominative singular in English is not clear; apparently the word was originally part of a prepositional phrase, like *e pluribus unum*. It is clear, however, that the plural of *rebus* cannot well be *rebi*, as it is sometimes thought to be.

The best-known type of rebus is the one in which pictures are to be interpreted in words. Another type, which ranks much higher as a puzzle, uses no pictures, but only letters and words, or occasionally numbers. Usually such a puzzle is based, at least in part, on the relative positions of its elements, and might be called a "positional rebus." Some good ones, on the other hand, involve no positional element. The following examples are some of the best of the non-pictorial, or literary and numerical, rebus.

1

What common word is this:

B
E

What word is this:

2

$$U \begin{matrix} C \\ T \end{matrix} U$$

3

What Biblical character is named here:

$$\begin{matrix} J \\ AH \end{matrix}$$

4

What is the full name of this girl?

$$\frac{Mary}{2000 \text{ pounds}}$$

5

Read this name and address:

Wood
John
Mass

6

This is one of the best-known rebuses:

$$\frac{STAND}{U} \qquad \frac{OATH}{UR}$$

7

Here is another old-timer:

$$\frac{STAND}{I} \qquad \frac{TAKE}{YOU} \qquad \frac{TO}{THROW} \qquad \frac{TAKING}{MY}$$

8

This one is more complex, but not too difficult:

9

This is perhaps the best known of all:

> If the B mt put: If it b full . putting:

The same rebus may be written this way:

> If the B mt put: If the B . putting:

The second form involves a term that may not be familiar to all people.

10

What five-word phrase is concealed here?

WETHER

11

What vegetable is this?

c sp h

GROUP B: LETTERS READ AS WORDS

In this small group of puzzles, letters or numbers are to be pronounced so as to make words. In some cases the pronunciation is somewhat strained.

12

Here is a four-line poem:

YYURYYUBICURYY4me

13

A railroad passenger wanted to know how long two certain trains would be in the station, and was told that one would be there from 222222 and the other would be there from 2222222. Just what was he told?

14

A man addressed this remark to a bottle. What did he say?

O I C U R M T

15

Translate this bit of dialog:

> *ABCD* goldfish.
> *LMNO* goldfish.
> *OSMR* goldfish.
> *OICD* goldfish.

16

This one is also a dialog:

> *FUNEM*
> *SVFM*
> *FUNEX*
> *SVFX*
> *OKMNX*
> *GUREZ*

GROUP C: PUNCTUATION PUZZLES

17

Punctuate the following:

In a school examination Mary where Jane had had had had had had had had had had had had the teacher's approval.

18

Try punctuating this one:

It was and I said not are and and and are are different.

19

This one already has some punctuation but it needs to be changed:

In came the soldier on his face; a fierce look on his feet; his shoes on his back; his armor shouting aloud his war-cry.

20

Punctuating this one should not be difficult:

That that is is that that is not is not is not that it it is.

21

Here is a sign for an inn. It needs not only punctuation but also a regrouping of the letters. The problem is to make an intelligible notice.

NOTICE
HERESTO PANDS PEN D ASOCI
AL HOU R INHAR M LES SMIRT
HA ND FUNLET FRIENDS
HIPRE IGN BE JUSTAN DK
INDAN DEVIL SP EAKOF NONE

22

To make sense of this short conversation one must supply punctuation, regroup some of the letters, and have a little immagination.

Civile ergo fortibus es en ero.
O nobile Deus nobus es Deus trux.

Section II: Anagram puzzles

As explained in an earlier section of this book, words or groups of words are anagrams of each other when they are formed from exactly the same letters. Thus *silent* and *listen* are anagrams. The puzzles in this section require the solver to supply such words in pairs or groups. Some of the puzzles are based on modified anagrams, called *progressive anagrams*, in which a new letter is added to the letters of the first word to form the second word.

23

The blanks in the poem are to be filled in with five different four-letter words, all formed from the same letters:

A _____ old woman, with _____ intent.
Put on her _____, and away she went;
"Oh _____," she cried, "give me today
Something on which to _____, I pray."

24

The blanks are to be filled with four words all formed by different arrangements of the same four letters.

> Landlord, fill the flowing _____.
> Until the _____ run over;
> Tonight we _____ upon the _____.
> Tomorrow go to Dover.

25

Here is a third poetic anagram puzzle. The words to be supplied are all formed from the same four letters:

> The cook is old, with hoary head,
> His years are quite a _____, 'tis said.
> Among the _____ he _____ away;
> His task is quite a _____ we'd say.

26

This puzzle, like the three above, requires filling in the blanks with words all formed from the same four letters:

> No _____ was there with cheerful light;
> The _____ raced round the ship all night,
> With _____ and wiles the sailors sought,
> But by the _____ not one was caught.

27

This is a progressive-anagram puzzle. Start with the word *am*; add any third letter and rearrange the three to form a new word. Then add a letter, shuffle the letters, and form a four-letter word. Repeat for a five-letter word and then a six-letter one.

28

Start with the word *at* and form progressive anagrams as described above to six letters. This word is relatively easy, and the problem can be solved in several ways. You might try adding letters beyond six; it is possible to continue to at least eleven letters.

Section III: Skeleton-word puzzles

In a puzzle of this type, a word or sentence is given with some letters missing, and the problem is to complete the words by supplying the missing letters.

29

Make a sentence by inserting a single letter eleven times among the following letters:

I E M E F A E D I I E I I G S

30

Insert a single letter among the following as many times as necessary to make a sentence. The spacing given is not to be followed:

A DEN I I CAN DOCK

31

By inserting a single letter a sufficient number of times, you can make sense of the following:

ALHOUGHHEWOOSIERED
HEYOLDHEOFOLDALE

32

Insert the same vowel a sufficient number of times and get a little poem:

PRSVRYPRFCTMN
VRKPTHSPRCPTSTN

Section IV: Miscellaneous word puzzles

33

Take the letters ERGRO. Add three letters in front of these letters and the same three letters in the same order after them, thus forming a common word.

34

Name a word that has the vowels *a, e, i, o, u* in order.

35

What common word contains one vowel six times, and no other vowel?

36

What nine-letter word contains only one vowel?

Section V: Solutions to word puzzles

1. Bone (*B* on *E*).
2. Continue (*C* on *T* in *U*).
3. Jonah (*J* on *AH*).
4. Mary Overton (*Mary* over *ton*).
5. John Underwood, Andover, Mass.
6. You understand you are under oath.
7. I understand you undertake to overthrow my undertaking.
8. A little misunderstanding between friends (A little *m* is under *stand* in *G* between friends).
9. If the grate be empty put coal on; if it be full, stop putting coal on.
10. A bad spell of weather.
11. Spinach (*Sp* in a *ch*)
12. Too wise you are, too wise you be;
    I see you are, too wise for me.
13. One train was in the station from two to two to 2:02, and the other was there from two to two to 2:02, too.
14. O, I see you are empty.
15. Abie, see de goldfish.
    Hell, them ain't no goldfish.
    O, yes them are goldfish.
    O, I see de goldfish.
16. Have you any ham?
    Yes, we have ham.
    Have you any eggs?
    Yes, we have eggs.
    OK, ham and eggs.
    Gee, you are easy.
17. In a school examination, Mary, where Jane had had "had had," had had "had." "Had had" had had the teacher's approval.
18. It was "and" I said, not "are," and "and" and "are" are different.
19. In came the soldier, on his face a fierce look, on his feet his shoes, on his back his armor, shouting aloud his war-cry.
20. That that is, is. That that is not, is not. Is not that it? It is.
21. Notice. Here stop and spend a social hour in harmless mirth and fun. Let friendship reign. Be just and kind, and evil speak of none.
22. "See, Villy, 'ere go forty busses in a row."
    "O, no, Billy, dey is no buses. Dey is trucks."
23. Vile; evil; veil; Levi; live.
24. Pots; tops; stop; post.

25. Span; pans; naps; snap.
26. Star; rats; arts; tars.
27. One solution: am; mat; meal; steam; stream.
28. One solution: at; rat; rate; later; relate.
29. Insert the letter *n* and get: Nine men fanned in nine innings.
30. Insert *m* and get: Mad men mimic and mock.
31. Insert *t* and get: Although the two tots tittered,
    They told the oft-told tale.
32. Insert *e* and get: Persevere ye perfect men;
    Ever keep these precepts ten.
33. *UND ERGRO UND*
34. Abstemious, or facetious.
35. Indivisibility.
36. Strengths.

Chapter 19

RIDDLES AND CONUNDRUMS

THE WORD "RIDDLE" IS OF RATHER UNCERTAIN DEFINITION, BEING applied to a considerable variety of puzzling questions and statements. The best known kind of riddle is the *conundrum*, which is based on a pun; the pun may be either in the answer or in the question. Many riddles, while stated as questions, are really not intended to be answered, but merely to offer opportunities for clever statements or "wise-cracks" by the questioner. The following list of riddles is divided into conundrums and other riddles. The collection is not further classified, except that those on two or three subjects are segregated.

Section 1: Conundrums

GROUP A: BIBLE CONUNDRUMS

1. Who was the first man mentioned in the Bible? ANSWER: Chap. One.

2. When is baseball first mentioned in the Bible? ANSWER: Genesis 1:1, "In the beginning" (big inning).

3. Where, beside the first chapter of Genesis, is baseball referred to in the Bible? ANSWER: It is mentioned in at least two other places: where Rebeccah walked to the well with the pitcher, and where the Prodigal Son made a home run.

4. What are the smallest two things mentioned in the Bible? ANSWER: The widow's mite, and the wicked flee.

5. Who was the fastest runner in history? ANSWER: Adam; he was first in the human race.

6. At what time of day was Adam born? ANSWER: A little before Eve.

7. What did Adam and Eve do when they were expelled from the Garden of Eden? ANSWER: They raised Cain.

8. How were Adam and Eve prevented from gambling? ANSWER: Their Paradise (pair o' dice) was taken from them.

9. Who was the first great financier? ANSWER: Noah; he floated his stock while the whole world was in liquidation.

10. Which animals took the most and the least luggage into the ark? ANSWER: The elephant took most, because he had a trunk; the fox and the cock took least, because they had only a comb and brush between them.

11. Why could nobody play cards in the Ark? ANSWER: Because Noah sat on the deck.

12. When was paper money first mentioned in the Bible? ANSWER: When the dove brought the green back to Noah.

13. Who was the first electrician? ANSWER: Noah; he made the ark light on Mount Ararat.

14. In what order did Noah come from the Ark? ANSWER: He came forth.

15. Who was the most successful physician in the Bible? ANSWER: Job; he had the most patience.

16. What did Lot's wife turn to before she turned to salt? ANSWER: She turned to rubber.

17. Why should one be encouraged by the story of Jonah? ANSWER: He was down in the mouth, but he came out all right.

18. Why was Pharaoh's daughter like a skillful Wall-Street operator? ANSWER: Because she took a little prophet from the rushes on the banks. (Note that this is an example of the rather rare triple pun.)

19. Who was the straightest man in the Bible? ANSWER: Joseph; Pharaoh made a ruler of him.

20. What two noblemen are mentioned in the Bible? ANSWER: Barren fig tree and Lord how long.

21. Who are the shortest men mentioned in the Bible? ANSWER: Bildad, the Shuhite, and Nehemiah (knee-high miah).

22. What man in the Bible, beside Adam, had no parents? ANSWER: Joshua, the son of Nun.

23. When did Moses sleep five in a bed? ANSWER: When he slept with his forefathers.

24. Who was the greatest actor in the Bible? ANSWER: Samson; he brought down the house.

25. Why was St. Paul like a horse? ANSWER: Because he liked Timothy.

26. How do we know that St. Paul was a cook? ANSWER: The Bible says he went to Philippi (fill a pie).

GROUP B: ALPHABET AND SPELLING CONUNDRUMS

27. Why is the letter A like noon? ANSWER: Because it is in the middle of day.

28. Why should men avoid the letter A? ANSWER: Because it makes men mean.

29. Why is the letter D like a bad boy? ANSWER: Because it makes ma mad.

30. Why is the letter G like twelve P.M.? ANSWER: Because it is in the middle of night.

31. Why is the letter K like a pig's tail? ANSWER: Because it's at the end of pork.

32. Why is O the noisiest vowel? ANSWER: Because all the other vowels are in audible.

33. Why is the letter P like a false friend? ANSWER: Because it is first in pity, but last in help.

34. Why is kiss spelled with two s's? ANSWER: Because it always takes two to complete the spell.

35. Why is U the merriest letter in the alphabet? ANSWER: Because it is always in the midst of fun.

36. Why is the letter W like gossip? ANSWER: Because it always makes ill will.

37. Why is the letter Y like a young spendthrift? ANSWER: Because it makes pa pay.

38. What occurs once in a minute, twice in a moment, and not once in a hundred years? ANSWER: The letter M.

39. What is the center of gravity? ANSWER: The letter V.

40. What word can be pronounced quicker by adding a syllable to it? ANSWER: The word *quick*.

41. What is the longest word in the English language? ANSWER: The word *smiles*, because it has a mile between the first and last letters.

42. What is it that, when it loses an eye, has only a nose left?
ANSWER: The word *noise*.

43. What word of five letters has only one left when two are taken away? ANSWER: The word *stone*.

44. What is it from which you can take away the whole and still have some left? ANSWER: The word *wholesome*.

GROUP C: MISCELLANEOUS CONUNDRUMS

45. What automobile is what the woman asked about a hen? ANSWER: Chevrolet.

46. Which day is strongest? ANSWER: Sunday, because all the others are week-days.

47. What kind of dress lasts longest? ANSWER: A house dress, because it is never worn out.

48. What men are always above-board in their movements? ANSWER: Chess men.

49. What is the best paper for making kites? ANSWER: Fly paper.

50. What part of a watch has been used before? ANSWER: The second hand.

51. Where are the coldest seats in a theater? ANSWER: In Z-row.

52. What is the hardest soap made? ANSWER: Castile.

53. A New York man owns a cattle ranch in Texas, and the ranch is operated by his three sons. The name of the ranch is "Focus." Why? ANSWER: Because it is where the sons raise meat (sun's rays meet). This is another triple pun.

54. Why is a sick man improved when he makes a wager of five cents? ANSWER: Because it makes him a little better.

55. Why is a pleasure trip to Egypt suitable only for very old people? ANSWER: Because it is a see-Nile thing to do.

56. Why was the little drop of cider so sad? ANSWER: Because all his friends were in the jug.

57. When does a man wear a large watch? ANSWER: When he expects to have a big time.

58. When is soup sure to run out of the bowl? ANSWER: When there is a leek in it.

59. What is so rare as a day in June? ANSWER: Any day in March is apt to be pretty raw.

60. What shape is a kiss? ANSWER: A lip-tickle.

61. What was Joan of Arc made of? ANSWER: Maid of Orleans.

62. What is worse than raining cats and dogs? ANSWER: Hailing taxicabs.

63. How do we know that "Uncle Tom's Cabin" was not written by a female hand? ANSWER: Because it was written by Harriet Beecher Stowe (Beecher's toe).

64. Why is the interior of a theater such a sad place? ANSWER: Because all the seats are in tiers.

65. Why are you always so tired on April Fool's Day? ANSWER: Because you have just finished a March of thirty-one days.

66. Why will the people of Ireland soon be the richest in the world? ANSWER: Because their capital is always Dublin.

67. Why does a train never sit down? ANSWER: Because it has a tender behind.

68. Why should a man never swim in the river at Paris? ANSWER: Because if he did he would be in Seine.

69. What animal changes his size twice every day? ANSWER: A cat, because you let him out every night, and take him in every morning.

70. Why did the farmer name his rooster "Robinson." ANSWER: Because he crew so.

71. Why can hens lay eggs only in the daytime? ANSWER: Because at night they become roosters.

72. Why should a turtle be pitied? ANSWER: Because his is a hard case.

73. How could a timid girl turn to stone? ANSWER: By becoming a little bolder.

74. If a girl falls, why can her brother not help her to her feet? ANSWER: How can he be a brother and assist her too?

75. Why does a sculptor die such a terrible death? ANSWER: He makes faces and busts.

76. When is a doctor most annoyed? ANSWER: When he is out of patients.

77. What should you do when you split your sides laughing? ANSWER: Run until you get a stitch in them.

78. Why isn't your nose twelve inches long? ANSWER: Because then it would be a foot.

79. What is it that goes around a button? ANSWER: A goat goes around a buttin'.

80. What is it that is put on the table, cut, and passed, but never eaten? ANSWER: A deck of cards.

81. What has a foot on each end and one in the middle? ANSWER: A yardstick.

82. What grows bigger the more you contract it? ANSWER: A debt.

83. What do artists like to draw best? ANSWER: Their pay.

84. A man has a live goose on the top of a tall building. What is the quickest way for the man to get down? ANSWER: By plucking the goose.

85. What is the best system of bookkeeping? ANSWER: Never lend them.

86. What is the best way to make pants last? ANSWER: Make the coat and vest first.

87. What is the hardest thing to deal with? ANSWER: An old deck of cards.

88. What has eighteen legs and catches flies? ANSWER: A baseball team.

89. What makes the Tower of Pisa lean? ANSWER: It never eats.

90. Why is a prudent man like a pin? ANSWER: Because his head prevents his going too far.

91. Why is a dirty boy like flannel? ANSWER: Because he shrinks from washing.

92. Why is a boy who has ripped his pants like a speaker who says, "And in conclusion"? ANSWER: Because he's tored his clo'se.

93. Why is a nail in an oak log like a sick person? ANSWER: Because it's in firm.

94. Why is a room full of married people like an empty room? ANSWER: Because there is not a single person in it.

95. Why is a kiss over the telephone like a straw hat? ANSWER: Because it's not felt.

96. Why is a side-saddle like a four-quart measure? ANSWER: Because it holds a gal on.

97. Why was Blackstone like an Irish vegetable? ANSWER: Because he was a commentater (common tater).

98. Why is the heart of a tree like a dog's tail? ANSWER: Because it is farthest from the bark.

99. Why is a lollypop like a race horse? ANSWER: Because the harder you lick it the faster it goes.

100. Why is a mouse like hay? ANSWER: Because the cat'll eat it.

101. When is an owl like one of the Presidents? ANSWER: When its a-blinkin'.

Section II: Riddles without puns

102. What is the difference between a sewing machine and a kiss? ANSWER: One sews seams nice, and the other seems so nice.

103. What is the difference between a cat and a comma? ANSWER: A cat has its claws at the end of its paws, the comma has its pause at the end of its clause.

104. What is the difference between some people and a mirror? ANSWER: Some people talk without reflecting, while a mirror reflects without talking.

105. What is the difference between a man going up stairs and a man looking up stairs? ANSWER: One is stepping up the stairs, the other is staring up the steps.

106. What is the difference between a greedy man and a hungry man? ANSWER: One eats too long, the other longs to eat.

107. What is the difference between a beautiful girl and a mouse? ANSWER: The girl charms the he's, the mouse harms the cheese.

108. What is the difference between a blind man and a sailor in jail? ANSWER: One cannot see to go, the other cannot go to sea.

109. What is the difference between sixteen ounces of butter and a pianist? ANSWER: One weighs a pound, the other pounds away.

110. What is the difference between a jeweler and a jailer? ANSWER: One sells watches, the other watches cells.

111. What is the difference between a man who is broke, and a pillow? ANSWER: One is hard up, the other is soft down.

112. What is the difference between a hill and a pill? ANSWER: One is hard to get up, the other is hard to get down.

113. Would you rather an elephant attacked you or a gorilla? ANSWER: I'd rather he attacked the gorilla.

114. Three large women were walking under one umbrella, but none of them got wet; why not? ANSWER: It wasn't raining.

115. What always happens at the end of a dry spell? ANSWER: It rains.

116. What is the surest way to keep water from coming into your house? ANSWER: Don't pay your water bill.

117. When will water stop running downhill? ANSWER: When it gets to the bottom.

118. What has eight legs and sings? ANSWER: A male quartet.

119. If you saw twenty-one birds sitting in a tree and killed one-seventh of them with one shot, how many would remain? ANSWER: The three that you shot; the others would fly away.

120. When is a black-and-white spotted dog most likely to enter a house? ANSWER: When the door is open.

121. Why do white sheep eat so much more than black ones? ANSWER: Because there are so many more of them.

122. What was the highest mountain before Mt. Everest was discovered? ANSWER: Mt. Everest.

123. Why is it that when you lose something you always find it in the very last place in which you look? ANSWER: Because you stop looking when you find it.

124. What is it that no man wants, but no man wants to give up? ANSWER: A bald head.

125. What grows larger the more you take from it? ANSWER: A hole.

126. Why are a girl's kisses like olives in a jar? ANSWER: Because after you get the first one the rest come easy.

127. Which burns longer, a wax candle, or a tallow candle? ANSWER: Neither; they both burn shorter.

128. How many pancakes can you eat on an empty stomach? ANSWER: Just one; then your stomach is no longer empty.

129. What does a hippopotamus have that no other animal has? ANSWER: Baby hippopotamuses.

130. In what month do women talk least? ANSWER: In the shortest month, February.

131. Is it all right to write a letter on an empty stomach? ANSWER: Yes, it's all right, but it is better to write it on paper.

132. When is it proper to serve milk in a saucer? ANSWER: When you feed the cat.

133. If two is company and three is a crowd, what are four and five? ANSWER: Nine.

Index

Index

Index

Index

Index

Index

Index

Index